Contents

Editorial

Well, we made it and another issue is here – back in its usual August slot. Normal service has resumed!

As we kick off issue 18, we're delighted to have the opportunity to bring you something a little bit different. The *Gutter* team are thrilled to be partnering with the Edinburgh International Book Festival for this issue: introducing *The Freedom Papers*, a collection of essays and works from writers and artists around the globe. Launching at The Edinburgh Book Festival in August 2018, this project pushes boundaries to explore ideas of freedom from different individual perspectives. You'll notice *The Freedom Papers* is smartly packaged as a supplement to our usual issue, and will be winging its way around the world to festivals in Brazil, New Zealand, Kenya, Canada and Scotland, as well as being available online. This thought provoking and – we hope you'll agree – important work poses the question, 'what does freedom mean to you?'

As we go to press, online freedoms are in the news. The Facebook data scandal highlights the stark opposition between the assumed freedom to like, share and socialise online and the harsh reality that the data trail we create is a valuable product to sell. We enjoy the freedom the web offers and yet, as users, we often unconsciously waive our freedoms of anonymity to clauses buried deep in terms and conditions. Having been bombarded with emails about the changes to data protection law, it seems clear that our digital footprint extends far further than most of us imagined. Essentially, the concept of the freedoms we think we enjoy versus the reality of that perceived freedom are somewhat at odds in an age when the internet, like the commons, has become enclosed.

Indeed, we can see contradictions between the web as the bringer of global democracy and freedom and the device by which elections can be handed to the highest bidder. With some countries heavily censoring their internet, clamping down on those who stray too far from accepted narratives, who is more free; someone under a regime where they can, quite literally, see their oppression, or, someone living in the Land of the Free where money silently manipulates the stories we are told and the views we hold?

Freedoms of passage through borders and the freedom to trade also become widely scrutinized as the UK prepares to leave the EU. Such freedoms we've taken for granted become significant as they are stripped away. And yet this lack of freedom is faced by millions of people around the world on a daily basis, as is beautifully illustrated in a selection of compelling essays within the Freedom Papers, and also in poems in this issue from Scottish PEN who via their Many Voices project, offer a creative outlet for voices that are silenced and marginalized and whose freedoms are restricted, be it by prison, refugee status or other circumstances. We have a range of Many Voices poetry to showcase in this issue and feel proud that we are able to celebrate this work and give the artists the opportunity to have their poetry read.

These are just some examples of how freedom can be understood, but how do we define freedom in the personal sense?

For Team *Gutter* freedom represents the ability to make decisions independently (we recently officially announced our status as a co-operative limited company). Working together as a co-op empowers fresh ideas, allowing us to move in a new direction whilst maintaining the standard our readers have come to expect. It also affords new opportunities such as this amazing collaboration with EIBF who have provided an incredible platform which should help increase our reach to a wider international readership and writership. A further international connection comes in the form of a story in this issue from the great Kenyan author Ngũgĩ wa Thiong'o. We are delighted to have collaborated with Jalada, a pan-african writers' collective, who are translating Ngũgĩ wa's work into languages around the world as an act of literary internationalism and decolonisation. We are grateful to Jalada for helping us to publish the story here in his own English translation of the original Kikuyu, and in the Shetlandic of Christine De Luca.

We are also incredibly grateful for the freedom facilitated by Creative Scotland, who have shown their support for Scottish new writing by providing us with funding, ensuring smooth production of *Gutter* for the next four issues. Excitingly, this funding means that, as of this issue, we are now able to offer payment to contributors. We feel strongly that it's important to recognise art as labour and having the opportunity to reward our contributors in some small way is a goal we have been working towards for some time. Hence funding comes at a critical time for this new collective, and ensures we can makes best use of our resources and continue to deliver quality content to our readers, whilst allowing us the freedom to operate in an open and fair way.

Prior to these exciting developments, the team were hard at work on the previous issue of *Gutter* and we are incredibly proud, with limited resources and a completely alien way of working, to have been able to keep *Gutter* afloat. At this point we are compelled to issue a groveling apology to those of you who unfortunately spotted the odd typo, mis-spelling or general editing fail within the pages of issue 17. We do take any errors extremely seriously and can only apologise wholeheartedly to the few people whose work was affected. You can see their work in all its typographically correct glory on our website. But, onwards! Did we mention that we can pay you now?

A new issue brings a whole host of exciting new literary talent. New contributor Catherine Simpson reflects on the trappings of marriage in *The Copper Ring*, whilst Nicholas Stewart explores what's left behind in death in *An Empty House*. For poetry, we have a stunning submission from Maria Sledmere and contributions from Bridget Khursheed and Charles Lang alongside solicited work from dynamic spoken word artist Hannah Lavery and a whimsical prose piece *Pale Ale, Green Tea* from long-time *Gutter* contributor and reader favourite, Billy Letford.

We're now excited to look to the future of *Gutter*, learning from the insights of writers around the world and buoyed by the wonderful support we've received from Creative Scotland and the Edinburgh International Book Festival. We hope that this issue acts as a fair representation of literature breaking down borders, embracing inclusivity and allowing ideas to spread. An antidote to the internet perhaps, here you can read competing truths told slant, wonder at the limits of freedom and language, and do it all without fear that we're mining your data to sell to the Conservative Party.

We are incredibly fortunate that this wee mag is heading out around the world. To think that *Gutter* will find a place with readers in Kenya, and from the mountains in New Zealand to the favelas in Rio is truly mind-blowing and we are embracing this opportunity. We value the support we've received from you, our readers, old and new, who we cannot thank enough for your unwavering enthusiasm.

P.S. Feel free to bin (recycle) the mag if you don't enjoy it. We're all about embracing freedom of choice!

Credo

AC Clarke

I believe
in the inviolability of seagulls
the free parliament and assembly of germs
an orang-utan's right to silence
the freedom of sheep to roam

I believe
in the sun's madness, the moon's capacity for illusion
the kindness of sparrows
the autonomy of slugs

I believe
that the difference between humans and cabbages
is 30% water
that it is not possible to tread the earth
without bruising it
that the sin of Adam was knowing too much
that the sin of Eve is pretending not to know
that whales have no sounds for hatred
and are happy because they have no hands

I believe
that excess is the mother of invention
necessity the father of lies
that all I ever learned at school was fibbing
that religion works better in fancy dress
that Babel was the beginning of isms
that all the lost words hang in a cave
upside down like bats, that the day
they are woken will be a day of reckoning
that everyone will get the afterlife they expect

In Brixton Hundred

AC Clarke

– Variations on the Domesday Book, with acknowledgements to Hamish Whyte
  who gave me this idea

St Peter of Westminster holds Battersea.
Westminster Hospital my brother's birthplace
Earl Harold held it.
We lived in Battersea
45 villans, 16 bordars
so three up, three down houses
15 ploughs, 8 slaves, 7 mills
a hospital, a school, a library
woodland for 50 pigs as pannage
Battersea Park and Power Station
from a villan having 10 pigs, 1 pig
from a bus conductor a penny ticket
from a villan having 9 pigs, none
for a halfpenny in a sweetshop nothing

Geoffrey de Mandeville holds Clapham
On Clapham Common I caught sticklebacks
Thorbjorn held it of King Edward.
At Clapham Junction we caught trains for London
8 villans and 3 bordars with 5 ploughs
Arding and Hobbs, a magic shop, optician
50 acres of meadow. It is said
The man on the Clapham omnibus they said
that Geoffrey has this manor wrongfully
was the litmus test for the whole country.

The Abbot of Saint-Wandrille holds Wandsworth
Where you could smell the glue factory
through Ingulf the monk. Swein held it
competing with the gin distillery
held it of the king and could go where he would

and caught a bus to town in Nine Elms Road
It was then assessed at one hide, now at nothing
whose pavements offered not a single tree
It was and is worth 20 shillings
our shabby terrace now worth half a million

An Immigrant's Love Song

Agata Maslowska

My heart is not enough
My time is not enough
My breasts are not enough
My arms are not enough
Moja rada nie wystarcza
My love is not enough
My anger is not enough
My thighs are not enough
Moja twarz nie wystarcza
My fingers are not enough
My worry is not enough
My attention is not enough
Moja łza nie wystarcza
My love is not enough
My curiosity is not enough
My fear is not enough
Mój podziw nie wystarcza
My sadness is not enough
My hips are not enough
My mouth is not enough
Mój język nie wystarcza
My eyes are not enough
My love is not enough
Mój śmiech nie wystarcza
My seriousness is not enough
My playfulness is not enough
My love is not enough
Mój taniec nie wystarcza
My gardening is not enough
My cruelty is not enough
My toes are not enough
Moja miłość nie wystarcza
My desire is not enough
My love is not enough

My elbows are not enough
Moja depresja nie wystarcza
My perseverance is not enough
My ignorance is not enough
My obsession is not enough
Moja paranoja nie wystarcza
My mind is not enough
My poetry is not enough
My hope is not enough
Mój akcent nie wystarcza
My writing is not enough
My love is not enough
Moja miłość nie wystarcza
My love is not enough
My repetition is not enough
My love is not enough
My repetition is
My love is not

Scotland

Hannah Lavery

Scotland, you're no mine
and I don't want you. So go
ahead, say I don't belong

wi your sepia tinged cross eye
sweeping over all that swept away
blood stained, sweat stained, sugar
for your tablet, ya macaroon,
ya rotten, gobby, greedy, thieving
bastard you, sitting atop aw that shite
and broken bones weeping, poor me.

Fuck you

I will dance jigs on your flags
blue n white. Blue, white n red.
It doesne' matter, but
ya wee chancer, Fuck!

For making us complicit
handing us whip and chains
an officer's coat, a civil service pen
a Queen to love. And lay me out,

I love you

with your mountain thyme
and all your coorie in.
And you can say
I dinnae belong to you-

go on.

But I am limpet
ſtuck on you

So fuck you

for no seeing
one of your own.
I will here.
I will ſpill here
my blood and your secrets, bleed
into you, root and earth and you
forever pagan, will in the ſpill
and the seep, see all you really are.

So fuck you, my sweet
forgetful Caledonia,

with love, fuck you.

A Body and its Prayer

Alycia Pirmohamed

Again, the silence of this

negative quadrant.

Whirlwind of stars already gone.

The dark between
a body and its prayer.

Long build of spruce, tendril of smoke
on the side of a mountain.

How to spell grief:

prostration blue mosque valley of roses.

Somewhere,
the deer are spinning

into black holes. This dish of almonds

can only bring so much *barakat*.

I am waiting
to feel the whole milk sweetness

of my grandmother's ghost.

Bismillah and again
the morning,

and again the threads of saffron

bright red, I ache for you.

My Father Teaches Me How to Cook

Alycia Pirmohamed

My father told me my language
vanishes into the air

the same as it vanished twenty years ago
when my mother

plaited my hair and rocked me to sleep
with long vowels of silence.

We confuse silence with survival,
tongue with vulnerability,

but can never forget even svelte darkness
is darkness still.

Language, the vagueness of that word,
languishes in this poem

like a starling in its nest. *Kutchi*
remains at the edge

of the tree line, a scattering of rocks
eroding silently.

How I used to view my body as a weapon;
my mouth a red-tinged

blade, my skin the terrifying fuse.
How I used to treat it like a violence,

constantly turning the dial; *hush*.
My father leans back

only halfway through teaching me how
to marinate the chicken,

his shirt stained a deep yellow, the house
a plume of coconut.

His silence is a gap that widens like a
hungry mouth,

his silence becomes my silence.
At last, he reveals that what he wants to say

does not have an English equivalent

%

Dan Spencer

Sally has power.

  Power's with the people.

  And Sally is the people.

  So, Sally has power.

  This morning, the leaflet girl buzzed again.

  'Mind if I drop off some leaflets?'

  'That depends,' said Sally. 'Are you the good guys or the bad guys?'

  Ha-ha. Sally tells Pete about it.

  'Exactly,' says Pete. 'Don't say a word to the other side.'

  'Exactly,' says Sally. 'Don't even say how you're voting.'

  'Or say you're undecided,' says Pete.

  'Or say you're voting their way. Misdirection! Confusion!'

  'Exactly. Don't give them anything to use against us.'

  'Everything's power,' says Sally.

  Sally and Pete have picked a side. They're the good guys. They're part of something – a tiny part of something big and growing. If you aren't with them, you're against them. They know their percentage. They're tracking their percentage over the days and weeks, as it rises and falls, as it converges and feints away and closes in...

  The flat is filled with leaflets, posters, badges, pens, etc.

For weeks now, Sally's been talking. Talk's happening everywhere. Sally's talking to friends, and the friends all agree. In meeting places and living rooms, and on their devices and out on the pavements, they're talking. She's catching up with old friends and she's making new friends. The city's alive, like a café in a book. She's talking and listening and everyone agrees.

  Sally's voting for change, she says. If you don't like change, that's fine, but Sally's changing. Sally's voting for everyone, she says. If you don't like people, fine: Sally's not voting for you. Sally's voting for everyone, and everyone should have a vote. Yes, everyone. Yes, of course children should have a vote (and if the children vote Sally's way, is that Sally's fault?).

  Sally's not a nationalist. But she wants to live somewhere without injustice, inequality or hate. If you don't want that, fine, but Sally doesn't want to live with you, so Sally's voting to live somewhere else. Sally's voting to live somewhere everyone votes like Sally.

Sally's not a nationalist, but don't go singing the national songs, if you're voting against her.

She's not a nationalist, but your nation isn't her nation.

She's not a nationalist.

She's keeping the NHS.

Sally's in a crowd and the crowd is carrying Sally and Sally's carrying the crowd, and the crowd is bringing down an institution (one of the institutions), massing outside of this building, standing outside of this building, this institution, which stands like a glass brick, this building (which stands for the institution), a vast, glass Duplo brick glowing on the wide, low, river, and the crowd is shouting up at the institution because the institution let slip how it really feels, let slip what it really is, and they're wise to it, because 'institution' means 'the opposite of change', and now the institutions are worried, the institutions are regrouping, and the crowd is banging on the glass walls of the institution, because the crowd is bringing down walls, because walls are coming down, and I want to feel it, what Sally feels, to be with Sally in the crowd, feeling fantastic like that, feeling so true and fantastic, and I wish I could feel it, and I wish I could be there with all my friends, moving with this crowd and feeling what it feels, but I can't.

The next day, Sally talks to the friends who don't agree.

The friends don't want to talk.

'We're undecided,' say the friends, but you know what that means. The other side is keeping quiet – great, grey waves of silence coming from the other side. The other side aren't proud of themselves. If you felt how they felt, would you say it out loud?

Sally takes the Socratic approach?

'Where's your hesitation?'

'Where is it that you do agree?'

'And if this were solved, then would you?'

Unfortunately, Sally's friends are uninformed. Unfortunately, they've misunderstood Sally's ideas, because Sally's ideas are misrepresented in the mainstream press. And, unfortunately, the friends' ideas aren't theirs but were given to them, were dropped on their heads from above, from a great height, like large, heavy hats, covering the eyes.

'What they don't see,' Sally's saying to Pete, 'is that our ideas – the ideas on our side – are coming from the bottom up, whereas their ideas – ideas on their side – are coming from the top down. What they don't see is their side is about fear, whereas our side is about hope. What they don't see is we're a movement, but they're standing still. What they don't see is their side is binary, but not ours! They haven't thought it through. They don't want to think. They want to watch TV and drink and have babies.'

'Exactly,' says Pete.

'Babies are all well and good,' says Sally, 'but look what's happening in the world. A baby is a political act. Babies have never been more political.'

Pete agrees, no, he does. Pete agrees. They agree. Every evening, in the flat, they're having energising, thrilling conversations of ideas, where all ideas are possible, and even disagreement could be possible, but, no, Pete agrees.

The vote is tomorrow.

Outside there's a view of the street at sundown – late, late summer – looking how it never looks – the corner pub, the yellow tenements, the yellow church... and leafy outer sections of the park... and the golden, peopled pavement... everyone standing and walking and thinking and alive – like never before... moving in every direction... on the golden pavement, and in the grand and bronze and expansive shadows...

Later, Sally still knows her percentage. Her percentage is set in stone. Later, she's still powerful. She's still the people – ideas and hope and power glowing like embers all over the city. Losing feels like winning. Winning feels like losing.

She's stopped wearing the badge. But the campaign poster is still stuck up in the window. Who'd have a problem with that? What's wrong with nailing your colours to the mast? And if Sally still uses the campaign pen in weekly meetings at work, how can anyone call that 'divisive'? Who in their right mind would put in a complaint? And who really believes that comment boxes or ballot boxes should be anonymous?

Admittedly, Sally says less about it, these days.

Admittedly, she feels less of a part of it.

But she's part of Pete, and Pete's part of her.

Pete talks less about it these days, too.

These days, Pete talks more and more about that other thing, the thing which would be part of them both – 50% Pete, 50% Sally – and would grow big and strong like a beautiful idea, and would mean something, and would matter.

More and more, Sally agrees.

Uncovered

Swara Shukla

Funny, this, how the dark makes her notice more, fear more. It is so different from her own little Bengali village and its deceptive calm of the night; Delhi in the night is brutally honest, washing away all its daylight pretences and revelling in the raucous freedom of the dark. It feels like nothing is hidden, *she* isn't hidden. She attempts to sheath herself anyway, wrapping the drape of her sari tighter around herself, ducking her head, and quickening her steps.

She struggles to reconcile these roads with what she is so familiar with in the day. She shouldn't have dawdled in front of the house; they were obviously not going to change their minds. It wasn't worth risking the dark for. She has been in Delhi nearly a year now, she should know better. The rich have certain luxuries she can't even begin to imagine – the luxury of whims and fancies, the luxury to turn a deaf ear. She has none; no luxury of truth, of defence, of explanations. No luxury to be heard.

She refuses to let fall the tear clinging to her lower eyelash. Right now, she needs to focus on getting through this labyrinthine war zone of leering gazes and lecherous shouts. She pulls the fabric of her sari closer. She feels someone's breath prickling the hairs at the back of her neck. She must be imagining it, has to be –

She curses herself when she realizes she has turned to look. Where were her reflexes this morning? Her annoyance morphs quickly into horror as she realizes she has taken a wrong turn somewhere. Damn this city and its duality. The sari is sticking uncomfortably to her skin now, the oncoming panic adding to the rivulets of perspiration sliding down her body. She still holds on to the cloth like a lifeline, not willing to expose any inch of her skin to more unwanted touches. She can't quite contain a snort at how futile her effort really is; what part of her modesty can she possibly hope to cover with a tattered cotton sari of all things? She will have to get used to this too now, she supposes – the futility and the discordant need to keep trying.

She stands rooted in the middle of the unfamiliar alleyway, her eyes seeking a non-existent friendly face. She gives another derisive huff at that – friendly face. Sinha *bhaisaab* was a friendly face, was he not? Maybe she should be looking for the exact opposite; a sneer instead of a warm smile; cold grey eyes instead of twinkling browns. She searches with renewed fervour. Now that shouldn't be futile, not in this miasma of human depravity choking the city. She narrows her eyes at a pot-bellied man sprawled out on the pavement a few feet ahead, puffing at a beedi and eying her with bloodshot eyes. His hands are calloused, blackened; his shoulders bony and collarbone jutting out in a jarring contrast to the flabby stomach his shirt-buttons are straining against. He reminds her of her husband. It isn't a comforting thought.

She walks towards the man. He makes no move to stand up when she towers over him, opting to crane his neck upwards to keep his deadened gaze on her. She suppresses the cough grating against her throat at the reek of the beedi.

Bhaisaab, she says, cringing at her choice of address. Did she honestly call him 'brother' – that inane word that women like her use as a flimsy shield to hide behind? She'd just had that shield snatched from her in the morning, it won't do to seek the warmth of false security again. She clears her throat. *Which way to Amar Colony?*

You have taken the wrong turn madam, he croaks, his face still stoic.

You don't say. He finally laughs at that, his eyes crinkling at the corners, making him look human for a fleeting moment.

Walk back to the point you turned at, turn left to get back to the path you were walking on and keep walking straight till the chauraha, and that is where you need to take the left turn.

She frowns in anticipation when he makes no further move. She loosens the grip on her sari, just a little. She mutters a *thanks*, the word foreign on her tongue, and walks on as he has directed. When she reaches the turn, she looks back over her shoulder. He is still there, hunched over, his beedi in hand. His face is turned downward, shadowed by the eerie chiaroscuro the golden light of the streetlamp overhead bathes him in.

She doesn't allow her lips to curve into a smile, doesn't allow herself to feel the inordinate relief washing over her. She bows her head again, and plods on.

*

She stares at his taut back turned towards her on the bed. He maintains a careful distance between them now. Even when he is on top of her, grunting liberally, he keeps his arms planted firmly on either side of her head, never touching; a hair's breadth between their faces, their gazes hard, their breaths mingling, their mouths never meeting. It is always quick, always rushed, a gossamer-thin closeness that snaps the minute he rolls off and turns his back to her.

Today he'd got into bed, and skipped right to the turned back.

Sometimes, she finds herself craving these meagre scraps of intimacy. Sometimes she is downright repulsed by them. Maybe it's the weight of expectations that's been lifted from even this part of their lives. They never got around to visiting a clinic. Aside from the fact that they didn't have the money, they were both afraid to have someone to fault for certain. She finds it better this way. There is no sense in burdening another life, or to have another life burdening them.

She tries not to think of the feather-light touches Sinha bhaisaab had bestowed on her. She shivers, berating herself for still feeling the ghost of his fingertips on her neck.

He had been gentle. She hasn't been touched like that in a long time.

It wasn't my fault, she whispers. *It wasn't, was it?* Regardless, she needs him to hear it.

Go to sleep Mahi. We'll talk in the morning.

Did you find any work today?

No. Couldn't get to the contractor's bike fast enough. Same story. Go to sleep.

They threw me out. I can't bring in any money anymore. You'll have to find something.

Maybe you should have just let him fuck you then.

She realizes she isn't really surprised. They don't have anything sacred, not anymore; nothing she feels might get tainted if she shared it with anyone else. The money she was bringing was the only tenuous thread holding them together, keeping them afloat in this cesspool of crushed dreams and broken promises. It is like cold water to her senses – the clarity of her realization. She slides down to lie on the bed, turning on her side to face her husband's back.

She studies the broad-shouldered expanse of his body. She reins in the sudden urge to reach out and touch, to anchor herself back to this reality, this little shack with the falling-in tin roof that she is supposed to call home. To this man who had proclaimed his love for her in front of a dozen people back when their village was still plentiful and their fields were still green; giving her the film-y love-story that she had fantasized about as a pigtailed thirteen-year-old stealing money from her mother's "secret" pouch to watch pirated Bollywood movies on the village projector.

He had been a true knight-in-shining-armour; she wonders now if she was only ever in love with his ambitions. He had promised her treasures of the cityscape, an escape from the shackles of the walls of her hut and kitchen, of the steadily reducing patches of swaying harvest in her father's fields, of the stagnancy of their hand-to-mouth existence.

She had admired him so much in those moments, when he got caught in the throes of his impassioned speeches and declarations. She'd marvelled at his capacity to dream, at the sheer magnitude of them. Even as their fields had started to dry up, and the money trickling in had steadily lowered, his conviction hadn't wavered, and neither had her faith in him.

When they'd got to it, eventually, it hadn't been the Grand Escape they had been planning for. It had ben desperate; a panicked frenzy unleashed by her father's limp body hanging from a noose suspended from their ceiling fan; the wailing of their sisters and brothers and mothers and nieces and nephews and the sight of the growing infertility of their lands, of the sheer helplessness at seeing their sole livelihood slipping away. And that was what her long-cherished dream had been reduced to; an endeavour shaped by their basest need to fill their rumbling stomachs.

She had still clung to the hope she had been nourishing over the years. Delhi hadn't welcomed them with open arms, but there had been something about the proximity of the towering buildings, the shine and splendour that had heretofore been images on a dirtied projector-screen, that had retained some of the dream-like quality, some semblance of the fantastical.

I will make these buildings someday, you see. I will be a constructor, and I'll build a house like this for us and our future children to live in, he had said, staring up at a building decked up with a glass-front, a huge wide board with black letters that were indecipherable to them.

She'd turned to look at him, her eyes roving over his sculpted body, hauling all their paltry possessions with an ease she had been smitten and blinded by.

You are made for this work, she had told him, grinning proudly.

But like it always does, reality had intruded, and the sparkle in his eyes, the bounce in his steps, the passion in his voice had gradually diminished. Maybe that's why the rightful place of fantasies is in the mind– an unrealized world residing firmly in the realm of the imagination.

She lays a palm on his upper shoulder and dares to shift closer. He doesn't flinch, makes no movement to show he has registered her touch. She doesn't know if he is asleep. She can't tell these things anymore.

It is not your fault, she whispers to the back of his head. She hopes saying it out loud would convince her more of the truth of that statement.

*

Her eyes ache with the effort of squinting them against the glare of the sun. At least the heat is dry today. She sweats easily, and she was hoping to drag this sari out through the entire week. Thank god for small mercies.

The bustle of the day is back, and she breathes a little easier; quite an ironic thing, seeing the plumes of smoke and the smorgasbord of vehicles clogging the roads. There are more beedismokers splayed out on the footpath. She pauses at the same spot as yesterday, peering around the edge of the wall. The alleyway looks as different as it is possible to be from last night, not that she's surprised. It is teeming, flanked by more oddly-proportioned men.

The silence is at loggerheads with the cacophony on the road behind her. Their heads are upturned, looking at her with glazed eyes. She frowns, momentarily confused; the quiet feels anticipatory, like a collective intake of breath. She gets her answer a minute later, when a low thrum of an engine is preceded by a motorcycle appearing in her right peripheral vision. She jumps, and steps aside to let the vehicle through.

The group on the pavement comes to life like a flock of bees as soon as the bike stops in their midst. She can't see his face, but the man on the bike is portlier, decked up in a crisp white shirt. She knows who he is.

Need two workers for Lodhi Road! He hollers to the group at large. It's a near-stampede, with the men tripping over each other in a mad race to get to the bike. The ones in the forefront conveniently forego the rush to start clambering on the vehicle even as the contractor pushes them off roughly.

200 rupees for the day. He glares at a lanky boy – evidently still in his teens – trying to get back on the rear-seat of the bike. The boy falters, and even though only his profile is visible to her from this angle, she can imagine the unspoken imploration on his face as he considers the contractor.

350? the boy tries, his voice meek, pre-empting the dejection from what he knows is a fruitless bargain.

Can't do more than 200, he insists, his tone softer.

The boy slumps his shoulders, a second too late; two of the men have weaved their way through the crowd to leap on to the motorcycle, holding their rusted pickaxes aloft, nodding vigorously at the quoted price. The contractor shrugs and raises his hand up to stall any others from coming forward. He swings his legs back over his bike to perch as far as possible from the bodies now clinging to it, and roars the engine back to life. He swerves to head back out of the alleyway, scattering the veritable throng, and disappears out of sight.

The entire thing takes a little over two minutes.

The men slouch back to their previous positions. She knows no one here, yet each of them is hauntingly familiar – she sees them in her husband every night.

She forces herself to look away and keep on walking on the right path. Forces herself to relax her fingers that are bunching up the cloth of her sari. She lets the hot gusts of wind slide the pallu off her head.

The veneer of the day is fading. It was the prospect of invisibility in these swarming streets that used to be a source of comfort for her. She juts her chin out, tries to straighten the spine hunched out of habit. She isn't sure she wants to be invisible now. She can't see the point anymore.

*

He is clearly shocked to see her. She isn't sure why. He used to be so pleased to have her around.

Bhaisaab, she pleads, not even bothering to correct the term. Her hands are joined in supplication; meek, not defensive, not invisible.

He frowns at her. His eyes no longer crinkle in a smile at the sight of her, don't rove over her like they had done before, don't twinkle, the warmth seeming to have seeped out of every pore of his body.

We hired another bai. You are not needed anymore. He shuts the door in her face.

She lets her shoulders droop, surprised to find herself unsurprised yet again. She is stagnating in her own disillusionment now.

She turns back to exit the courtyard and nearly collides with a girl coming in.

Sorry, didi, she mutters, keeping her eyes downcast. She is dressed in a similar burgundy cotton sari, still untorn, still unstained. Her pallu is folded and pinned up neatly over her shoulder, exposing her curvy midriff. She couldn't be a lot younger than her.

You the new maid? Not that hard to guess really.

The girl jerks up her head to meet her eyes; she is like an eleven-months-ago version of her own self, her wide-eyed wonder and capacity to be surprised still intact.

Y-yes, she squeaks, her gaze taking in her appearance, making her own guesses.

Go on then. Sinha bhaisaab is waiting for you. The girl nods and scuttles past her. She sighs and exits the gated entrance. She walks on and takes the right towards the girls' college. She stops outside the gate. There's the usual stream of students filtering in and out. They are different, all of them. They don't look replaceable, not with their easy gait and their highbrow chatter that she can't even begin to understand, hailing down the too-eager rickshaw-wallahs lined up along the raised footpath outside; they are utterly captivating in their insouciance, their lack of restraint. On good days, they spare her a glance and a warm smile; on most, she is happy to be a silent onlooker, to be able to toe the line separating her world and theirs, however briefly.

She positions herself nearer to the gate and peers up at the red-bricked building through the bars. The white letters are unreadable to her, even though the shapes have become so familiar. This is possibly her favourite place in Delhi, despite the chasm that exists between her and the women traversing it. It is the only space left that harbours the possibilities, the plenitude, the freedom Delhi had promised her. She wonders what it is like to get to step past these gates. Are dreams more attainable from the other side? Funny, how she feels most attached to a space she understands so little.

She looks left to find a bored-looking security guard leaning against his *lathi*, indifferent to the moving, chattering mass of women, no lascivious glint in his eyes. Friendly face, perhaps?

She glances back inside, at the sea of colours and echoes of laughter. At its raucous freedom, affordable in the daylight.

*

She is back – pulled in, as usual, by the wrong. This was supposed to be a wrong turn, the wrong path to walk on, and she still couldn't resist. Not after last night, and not after this morning. It is perhaps the magnetism of these dead-eyed people, glimpses into a world her husband never lets her into, even though it is as pointless, as despondent as hers; or perhaps simply the rareness of unscathed escape that it had provided her last night; or maybe the shrouded humanity in that man's eyes, or the quiet resignation in the boy's face today when he'd realized exactly what his inopportune hesitation had cost him.

It has just started to get dark; the crowd inside the alleyway is already thinning. She snakes her way through to the farther end, where she finds him again, slumped against the same streetlight. He raises her eyes to her, and she feels a tug at her heart when she sees a flicker of recognition there. He doesn't smile, doesn't shift his expression at all, but his eyes give her enough to let herself believe he had been waiting for her.

She approaches his somnolent figure, and after a second's hesitation, squats down beside him. He doesn't stop her, doesn't respond to her proximity in any way. Maybe that's what is different. His silence is incredibly freeing; she tests the waters by scooting closer, letting her shoulder touch his. He lets out a low grunt, half-hearted at best.

She chuckles, but doesn't say anything. She wonders if this is what her husband is on his way to becoming, his refusal to get out of bed this morning a starting step. If she'd get to steer them soon, take the reins of their existence in her own hands when his grip on them slips. Would that be so bad?

She eyes the man sideways. His eyes are closed and his eyelids are fluttering. She will ask him his name soon, his story. For now, she allows herself this little reprieve; this allure of mystery that she knows will be, like everything else, short-lived.

Pale Ale. Green Tea.

William Letford

The local pub, a snow filled Friday evening, perfect time to drink slowly, keep my feet by the fire and relax into the mellow. Even Danny Mcpake can't spoil it. Though it seems he's about to try. He pulls out the seat opposite and slides a shot glass full of green liquid over the dark mahogany table.

I'm fully committed to projecting dignity and happiness so there's no anger when I say, 'The hell's that?'

Danny delivers his reply with forced pride. 'Soors.'

'Thanks,' I say, 'but I've never been a Soors man.'

Danny sits up straight and throws back the shoulders. 'You'll never accept the fact that your father's gay, will you?'

I test the outside edge of the happiness. It remains intact. 'My dad's my dad, Danny. He's my hero, always will be. It's you that I won't accept. I've never liked you and why would the fact that you're seeing my dad make me like you any better?'

The situation he's referring to is a glorious example of the beauty of life. You're tramping along and you get to a certain age and you think, aye, I've got a fair grasp. Then the pin gets pulled on the emotional grenade that's been sitting beneath your family for forty years and boom. Tap those shoes together.

I pick up my pint and say, 'Cheers, Danny, have a good night.'

Danny lifts the shot glass and makes his way to the bar. He points his back toward me and that is the best place for bad news.

Now this is the truth, the revelation was a shock but it was the best thing that could've happened to my family. The catalyst for the explosion was the discovery that my mother had been unfaithful, more times than I would like to share, over the course of seven or so years. But why wouldn't she? She'd spent decades being starved of attention and when you near the footbridge of sixty you must think—well, hard to imagine what she thought.

Steady. Sip the pale ale and relax. Focus on the fire. If you're going to trudge through snow to get to the pub, a log fire makes the difference. When I look up Danny is glancing over his shoulder. He turns quickly and says something to Peter Hutchison. Peter leans back and draws Danny a mystified look. A good man is Peter Hutchison, and just went up a rung or two further in my estimation.

So the parents are finally free and good on them. The decision was late but at least it was made. And get this—a new love has bloomed. A love made from years of friendship and parenthood and precious shared experience. A joy in the realization that they managed to bring up two children and, despite the gin-throwing tie-burning arguments, be considerate and thoughtful. My mother's transgressions weren't forgiven. They were celebrated.

My father, in the physical sense, had been faithful, you could say devout, which was sad in almost every way but there was something in it that made me proud. There were however, ramifications from his monastic celibacy. He'd cracked out of the traps and went to work like a DeWalt drill switched to hammer. Which was also fine, when it comes to hammering we're all in the trade. The problem came when the work commenced closer to home than I would've liked.

Like Danny Mcpake, he's been nipping my brain for years. Nothing dramatic, he just manages to apply that consistent level of social discomfort. I smacked him once. On a Saturday two summers ago. I'd spent the day perfecting a beer garden tan in the Whistlebinkie's courtyard so I was a good few drinks down the chute and his wit was sharp and he was chopping me to pieces.

I lamped him. Hardly any back lift but it landed solid and he fairly flew. Worst thing I could've done. He would never lift his hands. Not in his nature. He'd whipped me on the verbal and I'd resorted to the bullying. He milked the punch and he's been working that ticket ever since.

When my sister, holding back the laughter, had told me dad was seeing Danny Mcpake I set the thrusters to full power and hit my dad's flat at light speed. 'Dad,' I said, 'What can you possibly see in him?'

He smiled gently. 'Son,' he said, 'absolutely nothing.'

The front door of the pub creaks open and a good waft of winter cold is sent toward me. Two regulars walk in, snow on their shoulders. The first one plucks off his wooly hat and he's practically bald, which is a great surprise, and this brings a raggedy cheer from the crew stuck to the barstools. The Borestone Primary has been infected by a clan of head lice and Archie Mutter's kids have been ferrying them back and forth to him and his wife for a couple of months. Obviously Archie got sick of the medicated shampoo.

The second regular is my father. I'm still surprised by the change. Every expression is brighter. He's himself, of course he is. But he's not the man I knew for the first thirty-odd years of my life. A strange sensation right enough.

Rita rushes up and the cuddle's almost a collision. She's had her eyes on him for nigh on infinity, and now that he's out, she can tease and flirt and get a feel for the fantasy without having to step around the fear. Her husband ignores the spectacle with a well-practiced turn of his shoulder. A whisky too much and he gets cursed with the wandering hands himself. Must've read many a Sunday paper with a good hard slap mark on his left cheek.

Dad's managing to peel Rita from the front of his body. He's nodding but he's got a hand on her shoulder and he's putting distance between them. He catches my eye. And there's the flicker. The breath before his face lights up. I smile to let him know I can see the Rita situation. He lifts a hand to his mouth and signals, pint?

I give the affirmative. I understand the disappointment. If I'm lurking as a witness he can't be as free in social situations. The man he was holds him back. People are taking turns to pat Archie Mutter's head. It's all part of the banter but some blows have the sting of an old grievance. Archie flails an elbow. My dad ducks through the commotion holding a lager and a pale ale. Archie has his chin thrust out but there's too much laughter for him to find somewhere to vent the anger.

Dad takes a seat and performs a slight bow to give the pint a touch of ceremony. The lager's in a tall glass and he raises it. 'To our sons having wealthy fathers and beautiful mothers.'

I say, 'Already there on the beautiful mothers, no?'

'To sons having wealthy fathers.'

I take up the toast. 'Wealthy fathers.'

'Rich on the bounty of life,' he says.

I get right to it because we've wasted too much of our life pretending. I say, 'Danny just told me I'd never accept the fact that you're gay.'

He tilts his head, looks at me like I'm a teenager. 'How's Sandra?' He says, 'How's the wee man?'

'You know how they are, I'm talking to you about Danny.'

He smiles the genuine smile. 'You know how Danny McPake is—you spoke to him. I'm asking about my daughter-in-law and my beautiful grandson.'

Bang goes the dignity and happiness. I say, 'He's using the situation to get at me.'

'The situation?'

'Aye, the whole situation.'

He looks at the dregs left in my last pint. He looks at the freshly poured soldier he's placed in front me. He says, 'Are we needing to take it easy on the Sheepherder's Gold?'

I loosen another button on my shirt. Maybe this is too close to the fire. I take a drink and tip the glass so far back I have to wipe my top lip with the back of my hand. I say, 'Been a hard week. Working out in the Yetts. Building site's a battlefield.'

He narrows the eyes. 'Are you on top of it?'

'Not a man there I couldn't lick with my good hand strapped to my side.'

'Good,' He says, and does this gesture. A waving gesture. Like he's swatted the bad thoughts away.

That's another thing, the old anger is gone, back in the day he'd have questioned me to the nth degree and washed himself with every detail. There's a short silence, awkward, as we both process his reaction.

I say, 'Remember you taught me how to punch. Remember the leather bag in the garage? You had me on that thing an hour every day. By the time I went to Primary my knuckles were like rivets. Christ, I was so small I'd throw everything I had and the bag would stay still and I'd bounce back two feet.'

He takes a drink and goes thoughtful.

I say, 'I've got a bag in the spare room. Put the wee man onto it already. Won't have him on it for an hour. Always thought that was too much but he'll be throwing his fists everyday. Best way to learn, eh?'

His eyes dance left and right. Then they lock on, front and center. 'Is this the conversation you want to have?'

I draw back, stare at the fire. 'It's Friday night,' I say, 'I just want to relax.'

He says, 'You're angry.'

'I'm not angry. I'm happy.'

He says, 'It's not about Danny Mcpake.'

'Absolutely one hundred percent stamped on guaranteed it's about Danny Mcpake.' A couple of heads turn because the volume has spiked. I lower my voice but I want to get my point across so I bite through each word. 'And if I am angry, it's because you put it there. Where was all this,' I do the waving gesture, 'happiness and don't worry when you were teaching me to smash men's teeth and take second seat to no one.' I throw back the pint of pale ale and when I look at the glass it's almost empty. I've drunk half the pint in two gulps and there's an engine fired up behind my eyeballs. You'd need a tractor and a towrope to pull down my eyelids.

He says, 'Stand tall enough and you can see everything from above. Be bigger.'

I hear the words but I'm projecting myself into the future. I see my fist smashing down onto the mahogany table, splinters of wood and lager and pale ale everywhere.

'Jamie', he says, 'Jamie.'

The table is in one piece and the lager and the ale are still there so I take another drink, a short one, a sip.

His phone is out and his thumbs are going and he says, 'Let's go for a walk in the snow.'

'A walk, are you a madman?'

'I'm a Morrison, am I not?'

I nod to the bar, 'What about him?'

He gives me the tilt, but there's kindness in the expression. He says, 'Danny's acting out because we're done. He's too young. Too young in the head.'

'Okay then, at last, some sense.'

'Seems like you've got an opinion, who would you have sharing my bed?'

It takes me two seconds to realise he's joking.

Outside the snow has stopped and the sky has cleared. Stars everywhere, breath blowing out in front of us.

He says, 'Let's go to the flat, your mam's coming over.'

'At this time?'

'I've sent her a message. She's up. We can have a green tea.'

'Green tea? Whose cupboards you been raking?'

'It's good for you.'

'Sugar and milk and I'll give it a bash.'

He says, 'It's not that type of tea.'

I'm thinking about who should be sharing his bed and I'm taking it serious and I say, 'I'll set you up with somebody.'

He grabs me by the shoulder and looks at me. Gives me a good strong cuddle. He says, 'Lets get some green tea down you.'

Obituaries

Sarah Whiteside

1

He was a fencer but not the *en garde* sort. That was the joke about him in the pub, him parrying and feinting after a pint or two then running the barmaid through with an imaginary foil. They used to laugh, out of kindness mostly.

Truth was he put up fences. There was a call for it once. These days it'd be one big field to the horizon if they had their way. Shame. Years he spent out there on his own, returning nights to that cottage with its small windows, its stout and silent walls.

The job disappeared along with his ability to do it. Now his hidden battles are over. Boundaries remain intact. No family survives him, only the fences, miles of them.

2

If you lived in the town you probably would have seen her, though you might not remember. She wasn't one to put herself forward; it's the way she was brought up. Still, all those years behind the counter at the pharmacy meant she gave most of us advice at one time or another. Perhaps she discussed hay fever remedies with you, or kept her face in line when you went in for a bumper pack of condoms. A post-menopausal woman, dowdy enough, hardly worth your notice. Her name was Alice.

She had a secret love, a passion for birds, though you wouldn't have called her a twitcher because it was the commonest kinds she liked best: blackbirds and robins; the various corvids; sparrows; starlings. On winter weekends she used to go up on the hill behind town at sunset with her binoculars in hope of a murmuration. I'm probably making something out of nothing, but I did used to wonder whether it was the limitations of her own life that made her pay attention to the way a bird could gleam, or improvise song after song or, in murmurating, listen so intently along with its fellows that they could plunge across the sky wingtip to wingtip and never collide. It might have appealed to Alice, that, to see it was possible to be extraordinary and full of mystery, yet pass through this world almost unnoticed.

3

It wasn't meant to happen. Soph was barely an adult. She hardly knew the boy who was driving and they weren't going anywhere important. It was just that she fancied getting out of town after the pub. Apart from anything else Rhia had gone off at ten with Alan from the office saying they were going to put their bare feet in the sea, whatever that meant, and they hadn't come back. It wasn't exactly that Soph was jealous, just it was only the back of eleven now and this place was sucking the life out of her. She wanted to step out of it too.

She had already planned what she would say if he tried to kiss her or anything. She wasn't stupid. She knew how it could look, what he might think. But she couldn't face lying awake in the too-small bedroom hearing her parents snoring through the wall, those two distinct pitches that didn't make a chord. She had to do something and there didn't seem to be anything better on offer. The boy wasn't drunk, so no; she didn't have her seatbelt on.

Either her mum or her dad must have phoned the university to tell them she wouldn't be taking up her place. Philosophy it was. It was as good as anything, that's what she had said if anybody asked, affecting a nonchalance fashionable among the young, though anyone could see she was going places, that she was on a road somewhere.

It happened as they came round the first blind corner. She must have seen it before they collided. Perhaps there wasn't time to speak. The heft of it, the strength close up, those horns furred with something akin to moss: the closest she'd ever got to a stag. Like something lucky, almost, like good fortune you might gasp at: just seconds either side and they would have missed it.

It didn't make a sound or not one she could recognise above the screech of brakes and the breaking glass, the windscreen shattering into bits and flying outwards in the light forever.

4

The stag often went that way at night. It was known to him, the route, and that knowing was almost like safety; he had always been all right before and thought – if thinking is the word – that he might be again. Perhaps he stopped that evening for a scent: some sharpness, some sweetness, some irresistible musk. Perhaps a patterning of dark against dark among the heather drew him. He must have heard the engine, the roar filling him, though he couldn't have understood what it meant, his head rising casually to see what was coming.

5

Having cleaned the drip trays and wiped the tables Jean stepped out into the cold, locking the door behind her. The sense of foreboding she had felt all evening didn't leave her now as she tiptapped along the icy path in her kitten heels and turned towards home. She put it down to that poor girl's death last month, for which she blamed herself, not that she could have done anything to stop it. Could she? She'd been through it over and over. Thing was, she told herself, you expect a bit of flirtation, some banter, the odd person leaving with someone they hadn't come in with. If she had to intervene every time there was anything like that she wouldn't have time to pour the pints.

And of course being behind the bar meant she had her own share of battles to fight, though at least she didn't have to contend with John and his imaginary foil any longer. Even she would have known to say there was something Freudian about that if anyone had asked. That's what she was thinking – disloyally actually, because she'd always had a lot of time for John – as she slipped on black ice, fell, and hit her head on one of those daft bollards they'd put in to keep pedestrians safe. The hour being late and it a minor thoroughfare, it was a long time before anybody found her.

6

Mum never wrote anything down but she liked a good story. As she lay in the hospital bed those last days – often holding my hand, though we weren't as a rule a touchy-feely family – she told me tale after tale. It wasn't so much the folk I knew from childhood she dwelled on as those from earlier times, who I remembered barely if at all. It might have been the morphine but sometimes she looked over my shoulder as if she saw them there behind me, all the people of the town come parading through her room. 'You've always been good at writing,' she said. 'You'd better write some of these stories down, otherwise soon you'll be the one lying here, wondering what to do with everything that's in your head.'

She was the first person I told about the pregnancy. I wanted her to know before she died. She clapped her hands together in delight then looked around, as if searching for someone who might want to hear the news. 'You can't breathe a word of this to anyone,' she would say as she began.

Gossip is an old-fashioned word for a person and not a complimentary one, but I suppose that's what she was. She had a talent for it: both the remembering and the telling. I still haven't forgotten John and Alice from those days at her bedside, or Jean, or Soph. It's especially Soph I think of – 'that beautiful girl', my mother called her, 'and too young'.

'You try so hard,' she said then, 'but soon you're gone and pretty soon after that, you're forgotten. I wish I'd learned that sooner. I would have been less cautious.' And then, I remember, she laughed and I laughed with her.

7

At the twelve-week scan there was no heartbeat. By then we had already imagined a new life.

An Empty House

Nicholas Stewart

I often get the dead ones. Some of them are really grotty. Not as bad as the junkies and the alkies but. I also get lots of people moving on to other places, or into homes. But mostly dead ones in this town.

It's not a bad job. The lads are good. There's no-one really overseeing you. Not unless it's a special case. And there's plenty work. There's more than enough work. They could take on extra bodies, they could double up if they had the money for it. Because there's so few of us it means that some places lie empty for months before they even get seen to. It's about a ten year wait for a council house so it's a bloody waste to have them empty with a queue of folk waiting on them. But there's only so many hours in the day. We can only get through so many.

You wouldn't believe the amount of junk people build up. By the time you've got it all out and loaded up the van sometimes you cannae believe that you could fit it all in the one house. Or a flat even. The amount of shite you can squeeze in a flat. It's stuff in the main that doesn't get used. They hang on to all this stuff that's just taking up room. Lofts – lofts by Christ! If it wasnae for the weather I'd advocate flat roofs in this country because there's never a loft but it's full of crap.

Seeing all that rubbish folk hold on to makes you think, makes you look at what you're keeping yourself. I'm the same as anybody – used to be at least – buy stuff and don't know where to put it and stick it out the road and forget about it. And then it's just got a wee home somewhere. But then you realise it's room you could be doing with. You start running out of space and then it's like Tetris – naw, no Tetris, the ones where you slide the bits around to make space for other bits. That's what life is like, a sliding puzzle where the only open space is the one where you stand pushing the bit ahead of you to make space for the one behind. 'No,' I said to myself, 'No I'll not get like that. I'll not be like one of them.' I threw out a tonne of stuff. And now I'm careful about what I'm bringing in so's I don't get bogged down with stuff.

Not all of them hoard things like that. Some of them don't have much at all. You can run through the place with a couple of pairs of hands in a few hours. There was one like that that sticks in my mind. I think about it a lot actually. There was really nothing there. Not nothing, but nearly nothing. You know I've seen sights man, I'll tell ye, the way some folk live. Caked in dirt, and the smells, and the dirty needles, dead animals, you name it. Most of them I forget. But I think about this empty place quite a lot. I thought it was empty at least, but then I got into the loft.

It was an old woman. A dead one. That's all they said other than it'll be quick. Since it was gonnae be so quick they said go do it yerself. I said hold on a minute but they said don't worry there's nothing hefty. I said if I find out you're at it you'll be getting a call. I'm no howfing a cooker or a fridge-freezer or a sideboard down the street on my own.

The house was an old yin up in Nethermerton, built in the 40s or 50s I'd say. It was an end terrace and didn't have rough casting, one of the ones with the wee slit windows on the stairs. It looked common enough outside. The garden wasn't awfy tidy but it was October or November time so it wasn't really the time of year for a tidy garden. The door was an old wooden one with a round handle. That was strange cos all the council houses now have the UPVC doors. There was chib marks at the edge of it so I could tell they'd had to break in to get the body. I had the key for the new lock and I let myself in. It smelt a bit stuffy, a bit damp, but it didn't smell like death which was a bonus. It was all dark inside the hall, the doors were all shut so the only light was that coming in behind me. I went in and hit the light switch. An old tungsten bulb lit up behind a pink lampshade, a scalloped one with tassels. The walls got a rosy glow from the shade and the floor got the unfiltered yellow tinge straight from the bulb. The walls were papered with a floral pattern, the carpet was greyish and nearly worn through down the middle.

I passed the stairway and went in the first door I reached. It took me into the living room. It had the same carpet and it really was worn through in places. Beneath the small table with the single wooden chair and in front of the armchair the carpet was gone. Where it had been there were bare floor boards showing, trimmed with black underlay that crumbled to dust beneath your boots. There was blue floral paper on the walls and red velvety curtains across the windows. The curtains got paler the higher they got as the layer of dust got thicker and thicker. That was all there was in that room.

I thought I'd better check the kitchen next. I went to the door at the end of the hall. It had a microwave. The spaces for the fridge and the washing machine were empty. Wires were hanging out the wall where the cooker should have been. The first two cupboards I opened had nothing but dust in them. The third had a plate with a knife and fork and spoon sitting on it, and a thick glass tumbler upturned next to it. All the others were empty. I thought, 'Yaldi.' But it was a bit sad to look at. I thought maybe someone had been in and taken stuff away already, but there weren't any signs of it being cleared out all the same.

The bathroom was downstairs too. It had a murky light coming in through the frosted window. The walls were papered beige with a fake tile pattern. The bathroom suite was green – or avocado they call it sometimes. There was a rose coloured carpet down, it was rank: all crusty round the toilet bowl, all matted and stained. The handles on the bath were all rusty. The edge of the ceiling and around the window was all mouldy. There was a bar of soap next to the sink, half a roll of toilet paper on top of the cistern, and a yellow toothbrush lying on the window ledge.

I climbed up the stairs. On the landing was a bucket, the kind that comes with a mop but with the colander bit off. It was half full of murky liquid. I looked at the ceiling: no drips, no stains. Nudged the bucket and a whiff of pish came off it. There were three bedrooms. One of the doors was lying open. I didn't go in, I could see what I needed to see from the doorway. A wooden bed, the whitish bed covers left unmade. The curtains shifting a little from the draft coming in the window. A veneered chipboard wardrobe. A pile of books on the floor.

The other two rooms were bare. When I say bare, I mean empty. Completely empty. The carpet stopped at the threshold bar and there was just the floorboards beyond. There were no curtains. No lampshades, no light bulbs. Nothing.

There wasn't half an hour's work in the whole house.

I went back down the stairs to the living room, lit a fag, pushed the curtains fully apart and opened the windows. I looked out at the mossy garden path, watched a dog dauner up and take a pish on a lamppost at the front of the garden. I finished, stubbed it out on the window ledge and flicked it into the grass. When I turned around and noticed that there was a plastic tub on the floor behind the armchair. I hadn't spotted it earlier on. It was blue with a semi-transparent lid, like a big food tub. I picked it up and set it on the wee table. The table was square; about 500 by 500 or so. The tub was all full of paperwork. On top were letters: council tax, bank statements, pension statements. I could see she'd worked with the development corp – the pension letters were headed the Fishescoates Development Corporation Department of Libraries, Archives and Museums. There were utility bills as well. And beneath those was a birth certificate. Born on Lewis, 1937, at home. And then beneath those was an old wooden box with a hinged lid. I opened it up. It had wee blue cards in it, all the same size, with neatly ordered handwriting on them. I pulled out the first and read it.

> Item | Wooden bed frame
> Creator | Wm. Jamieson & Sons.
> Description | Mahogany veneered plywood and chipboard bed frame. Length = 203cm. Width = 199cm. Height of base = 68cm. Height of headboard = 103cm.
> Date | Purchased 06-02-1967
> Type | Essential
> Source | Gardner's Furniture Store, Jamaica Street, Stromo
> History | Bought by Henry and I to furnish our first home at Blueveigle Street, Stromo. Took up most of the room. Brought to this house on Bothwell Street, Fishescoates by van on ferry on 12-05-1971
> Location | Bedroom 1

Related (Active) | Mattress, duvet cover, pillow, duvet cover, pillow case, wardrobe.
Related (Deleted) | Bedside table.

I read through the next few.

Item | Chair
Creator | Unknown
Description | Pine chair with cushioned seat
Date | Purchased 06-06-1978
Type | Frequently necessary
Source | MFI
History | We bought this as part of a dining set, including a folding table and 4 chairs with money from our 10th anniversary gifts. Other parts of the set were discarded over succeeding years due to deterioration or superfluity. There are bite marks on the chair legs from Ruaridh. The seat cushion was reupholstered by me in 1991.
Location | Living room
Related (Deleted) | Chairs (x3), table.

Item | Cardigan
Creator | Me
Description | Green wool knitted cardigan
Date | Completed 21-12-1976
Type | Occasionally necessary
Location | Bedroom 1

Item | Training shoes
Creator | Hi Tec
Description | Colour: white, pink, green, black
Date | 07-01-1994
Type | Rarely necessary
Source | Your More Store
History | The sole has worn down at the sides of the heel and been patched beneath the ball of the foot with a washing up liquid bottle. Various splits in the upper repaired with superglue.
Price | £7.99
Location | Downstairs hall

Item | Ink pad

Description | Red ink pad in black plastic case
Type | Rarely necessary
Source | Stationary Box
Location | Living room:Tub

I read through the rest of them. There were 42 of them altogether.

Desk (Occasionally necessary)
Plate (Essential)
Knife (Occasionally necessary)
Fork (Occasionally necessary)
Spoon (Essential)
Glass (Essential)
Washboard (Rarely necessary)
Key (Rarely necessary)
Lampshade (Unnecessary)
Bucket (Frequently necessary)
Tub (Occasionally necessary)
Armchair (Frequently necessary)
Curtains (x2) (Unnecessary)
Microwave (Frequently necessary)
Duvet (Frequently necessary)
Duvet cover (Unnecessary)
Pillow (Frequently necessary)
Pillow cover (Unnecessary)
Wardrobe (Unnecessary)
Pen (Occasionally necessary)
Marker (Occasionally necessary)
Cellotape (Occasionally necessary)
Black dress (Rarely necessary)
Nightgown (Rarely necessary)
Underwear (x3) (Frequently necessary)
Socks (x2) (Frequently necessary)
Dress (x2) (Frequently necessary)
Black shoes (Rarely necessary)
Black overcoat (Rarely necessary)
Deletion stamp (Rarely necessary)
Hairbrush (Unnecessary)
Cardboard box (Unused)

Towel (Rarely necessary)
Dishcloth (Rarely necessary)

There were a couple I read that were interesting:

Item | Shearling coat
Description | Long-armed hip-length sheepskin shearling coat. Grey-brown colour.
Button fastened.
Date | Unknown, likely 1890-1920
Type | Rarely necessary
History | Belonged to my father and he said it was made on Lewis and that he had
inherited it from his father. He used to wear it in the winter when he took the dogs
into the hills. I can still smell him off it after all these years. I will wear it in the cold.
Location | Bedroom 1

Item | Blanket
Description | Cotton baby blanket. Pale blue. 46x74cm.
Date | 10-04-1980
Type | Unnecessary
Source | Woolworths
History | The only thing left of Thomas. I can still smell his smell on it after all
these years. It is dirty because I have tried to get rid of it. I have really tried.
Price | £1.50
Location | Bedroom 2

I went round the house with the cards, checking everything off one by one. I
brought them all down to the living room and laid the card on top of each one. After
15 minutes I'd collected everything in the house, including the bed and the wardrobe.
Everything collected took up a corner of the living room. I had 41. The blanket was
missing. I guess she must've managed to get rid of it in the end.

I collected up all the cards again, stacked them and put them in the box. I closed
the lid over, put it back in the tub and put the letters back on top. I sparked another tab
and thought about my folks while I smoked it. When I was done I opened the tub again
and took out the card for the baby's blanket and tucked it in the breast-pocket of my shirt.

I set to work packing up the gear that was recyclable and taking apart the bed frame.
I set it all out at the side of the house then loaded up the van. The books from the bedroom
were just library books so I chucked them in the wheelie bin. It all took half an hour.

Then I brought the ladders off the top of the van back to the house. I thought I better take a swatch up the loft just in case. Wasn't likely an old woman putting stuff up there but still. The loft had a narrow opening. I unhooked the latch, strapped my headlight to my dome and pushed it open. Dozens of papers came flooding out as soon as the gap was wide enough. I flapped at my face and wobbled on the ladder not knowing what it was at first, might have been a bird. But it was just some wee bits of card that must've been lying at the edge of the hatch. I pushed the hatch up again, but every time it was open enough more cards would come tumbling out. I thought 'fuck it' and just pushed it right up. A tonne came raining down on my head and shoulders. The floor was awash with them, these blue cards. When they stopped coming down I crept up the last steps and poked my head up through the hole. There were towers of cardboard boxes on every side of the opening, from the loft floor to the roof. A ridiculous way to fill a loft. Just spread them out, you know what I mean? I got up into it and managed to wiggle a toehold either side of the hatch so I could straddle the opening and drop the boxes down. Picking a box off the highest row I pulled it down slow – it was heavy – and looked at the flaps on top in the circle of light from the headlight. 'Deletions' was written on it in black marker. I lifted the flaps: more blue cards like the ones downstairs. Pulled out a handful. Same rows of neat writing. But on each one a red stamp: Deleted. One for a grater. One for an alarm clock. A pair of slippers. A shower cap. A glass jar. A shovel. A pack of tiles. Clothes pegs. A necklace. Book after book after book. I nudged the steps out the road with my foot and dropped the box to the floor. It bounced up and tipped over and the cards poured out onto the floor. Took another box down: more deletions. A medal for running. A mosquito net. A shoe horn. Chucked the box down, it spun over the edge of the last one and spilled its cards. Then another box of deletions. And another. And I could see behind that there was another column of them. I started just pouring the cards out the boxes and then throwing the box after them. Box after box after box. More and more blue cards spilt all over the floor, making a million triangles and diamonds of different shades, tints and shadows, covering the floor and toppling onto the stairs. I cleared the first layer of columns and had a path right round the hatch to walk on. The next layer was all more deletions. A wireless radio. A nit comb. A football. Cleared another layer to find another layer behind. A wok. A satellite dish. A porcelain figurine of a shepherd boy. The ladders keeled over with the weight of the cards against them. A dragon plant. A stapler. A postcard sent from Tenerife. The surface of the cards on the floor seemed to be rippling, a constant trickle flowing down the stairs now. And more boxes and more boxes, and more cards and more cards. And they heaved in waves on the floor, and the stairs were not visible anymore. And I don't know how long I was up there in the heat and the dust of it but there did come a point when I tipped out the last box and peered out at the river of cards below.

I rolled up my sleeves and half-dreepied down, and landed with a splash. I tried to wade through but the current was too strong and I got swept along, tumbling and bobbing along its course. I looked up and at the top of a bank I thought I saw a woman wave at me. She had white or maybe blonde hair that looked a bit purple in the gloaming. I couldn't get my hand up to wave back and a second later she was gone. Eventually I managed to drag myself out over the threshold of the front door. I lay on the path. Once I'd caught my breath I checked my pocket. My fags were ruined but the lighter still sparked. I tried to set light to the house but the fire wouldn't take with how sodden it was. I just thought the place needed getting rid of. You shouldn't make a home of a place that a river's run through. It'll only flood again.

What has two legs but can't walk?

Jacques Tsiantar

'I thought it was a wonderful joke, and I'm sure they did too,' says Mary.

She's sitting by the dressing table, plucking her favourite hairclip from her head. Her dyed curls fall to her shoulders and she places the clip by her jewellery box. Normally Mary's hairclip makes me shiver. The teeth clutch inwards like a dead spider. But right now, I don't care. Not with the dead dog floating behind my back.

It appeared a few hours ago, the instant I realised nobody laughed at my joke. Our dining partners– my boss and his new wife– sat in an awkward silence as it materialised above the table, one paw in the mashed potatoes. A greyhound from the waist up, sickly pallid with skin tearing in places, and not much else from the waist down aside from a few dangling segments of spine and hanging flesh.

It looks at me, now, in the reflection of the dressing table mirror. Skin stretched over the pointed, slight face. Its jaw opens, revealing black, clustered teeth.

I didn't think it was very funny, either.

A paw rests lightly on my shoulder, the nails, so long they start to warp and split, audibly scratching against the fabric of my suit jacket.

Dead dogs usually aren't.

'So, Danny's playing football tomorrow afternoon, isn't he?'

I try to shake off the spectre's paw, but it grips tighter, digging suddenly into my shoulder.

'Danny's playing football tomorrow, Richard.'

'Yes darling,' I reply.

Yes darling.

She removes her earrings and runs a fine brush through her hair. I like to watch her brush her hair. One hundred strokes, each night. There is nothing else she touches so lovingly.

When was the last time you fucked each other?

'Oh, Richard,' she says as I burst into fits of coughing, 'You must get yourself to the doctor for that awful cough.'

'I'm fine,' I say, swallowing down a dry itch in my throat, 'Too much wine, maybe.'

You hardly drank anything. Boss didn't like that.

'You'd better not be coming down with a cold, Richard. We don't want Danny getting sick.'

It was written all over his face. Like he couldn't trust a man who doesn't drink.

'I'm not, darling.'

I look past her, into the mirror. There I am; all five-foot-five of myself. A shadow under my belly, hardly any hair- at forty-three. I look at the small, wiry greys sprouting at my temples, where the dead greyhound's toothy mouth hangs, salivating on my shoulder. Thick threads dripping from its jowls.

Not much of a neck to speak of either.

'Anyway, I can't pick him up from school tomorrow, Richard, I have that meeting with the school governors, remember?'

'Ah yes.' I want to step out of the frame, but I can't stop staring at the greyhound. The thing's body, split where ribs protrude at the wrong angles, the tiny swellings of maggots moving underneath its skin. I look at its eyes– refracting the light like rock pools, an emerald-green sickness that I'm not sure I have ever seen, swirling with shapes I've never known. And its voice.

Richard.

It rolls its words between those rotten teeth, before expelling them with the rasping breath of a metal file over glass.

Go downstairs.

'I need a glass of water,' I almost shout, 'Do– do you want anything from the kitchen?'

It's about time we had a talk.

'No thank you, Richard.' The hundredth stroke finished, Mary lies the brush gently in its place on the dressing table, 'But could you make Danny's sandwiches for tomorrow? I was so busy today I forgot.'

'Yes darling.' I leave the bedroom, closing the door behind me. The greyhound follows, its drooping head melting through the painted wood. I don't try to outrun it, padding in my socks past the bedroom of my sleeping son.

Yes, we don't want to wake him.

The aftermath of the night's dinner lies on the table. Empty coffee cups, small stains of gravy and other indistinct liquids. My boss wasn't so much a messy eater as he was boisterous. Complimenting Mary's cooking with gusto. I noticed that she, the woman who sat next to him, hardly ate anything. She cut tiny slivers of lamb with her bone-white hands, just barely raising the fork to her mouth.

Who was that, his third, fourth wife?

Its breath seeps into my nose. Pickled meat and a whiff of diesel. It almost makes me gag, but I swallow. I won't give it the satisfaction.

They keep getting younger, don't they?

I go to the fridge and brings out packets of cheese, ham, some wet lettuce, and margarine for Danny's sandwiches.

I like that. The renewability of love.

As the greyhound bends to get a closer look at the shelves, I slam the fridge door. I know it won't do anything, but I need to slam something. The greyhound pulls its immaterial snout from the fridge door with little effort and goes to sniff at the packets in my hands as I take them to the counter.

Couldn't pilfer a bit of ham could I, darling?

I set them down and grab some bread. The kind that Danny likes. Pure white and the flavour of cotton. The greyhound floats onto the counter and rests, one paw over the other, watching me work.

I try to focus on the sandwich, how soft the bread is as I slather it with margarine, feeling it deform under the pressure of the knife and not springing back up.

She was a sweet little thing, wasn't she?

My butter knife tears through the bread. I hate this white stuff; it's like eating a slice of packing foam. Brown bread wouldn't do this. Proper wholemeal doesn't break on you. But Danny doesn't like brown bread.

And she had the best kind of dress.

Its tongue dangles from its maw, lazily flopping. Sometimes it moves its mouth when it speaks, other times it feels as though the words are being injected into my brain. I turn back to the sandwich. I don't want it to see me looking.

We could all see right down her cleavage.

I hear it lick its chops, and I'm aware of my tongue in my mouth, now. Thick and dry. I swallow as I butter a new slice of bread. For a moment, I have an idea of stabbing the greyhound with the butter knife.

That'd do it, Richard. Stab a ghost with a fucking butter knife.

You didn't have to be so obvious about it, though.

'I wasn't looking down her cleavage,' I finish buttering the bread, and reach for the ham. A twitching nose follows my hand. The greyhound pants, grey tongue slipping out to moisten its snout.

Yeah, right. We all noticed. It's like you wanted us to catch you at it.

The ham is clammy. I look at it glisten in my hand.

And when Mary asked you to fetch the wine, you really had to manoeuvre for that one.

I slap it onto the bread, hearing the wet thwack of soggy meat.

But then suit trousers are always bad at hiding erections, aren't they Richard?

Two slices. If I put two slices of ham in the sandwich, I can hide a piece of lettuce between them.

Oh, yes, give him a bit of lettuce. The fat shit needs it.

Pressing down another slice of the wet ham on top, I make sure no green edges peek out at the sides.

I wonder what your boss's wife thought of you.

She must have thought I was harmless. A harmless, middle-aged man. I cringe.

She probably thought it was cute, trying to get a peek of her breasts like that.

'I wasn't trying to look down her dress.'

The greyhound slinks around my back. It seems to drift about a bit more, now that we are alone.

Oh, but then you made that awful joke. She hated it the most.

My hands have started to tremble. I reach for the packet of cheese. There's a tightness swelling in my chest, a tickle in my throat like a dry hair stuck on the back of my tongue. The packet is unopened and, after a few attempts picking around the end for the tab, I grab a kitchen knife and stab through the thin plastic lid.

I saw her nipple, actually. When she bent down to pick up her fork. Lovely and pert and just flushed with colour, like a cranberry.

I will not cough, though the itch in my throat is maddening. The packet open, I peel a slice of cheese from the rest, waxy and malleable between my fingers. I place it on top of the ham, trying to line it up. An edge pokes out, so I break it off and eat it.

I went under the table for a while, to get a better look of things.

The cheese tastes of nothing, too.

Do you want to know what colour her knickers were?

I check the packet. Extra mild.

I'll give you a clue.

A bubbling of saliva gurgles at the back of its lacerated throat as its muzzle creeps closer to my ear. The cracks and splits in its voice are begging me to cough and splutter.

She wasn't wearing any.

I can't help it. I hack out a dry, painful series of wheezes. Whatever is in my throat doesn't budge. I feel hot under the collar of my shirt and undo the top button.

I could show it to you, Richard.

The greyhound turns, its muzzle twisted into a feverish grin.

Just a peek. You won't be doing anyone any harm.

'No thank you,' I say.

Something in the greyhound switches. With a jarring flail of limbs it rounds on me, teeth bared before my face. I have to grab at the counter, feeling for the first time an immediate fear of this thing. The knife clatters to the tiles below and the greyhound's green eyes glint sharply as it growls. Flecks of saliva whip and dangle, threatening to fling away.

Don't give me that shit, Richard. I know you're thinking about it. Is she shaved? What kind is it?

The tendons binding its jaws tug and its tongue extends, curling and twisting. I recoil as it snaps at me. Its voice rings, whining with an awful glee.

There are so many different types, after all. They're like flowers, aren't they Richard?

I steady myself on the kitchen island behind me. The greyhound advances slowly, its exposed ribs tugging at the flesh around them as it pants feverishly. I can hear the creak of bone, the strain of muscle.

'Shut up,' my voice fails me, cracking.

But that's not enough. You need to know– see it for yourself. I know you do. We males want the truth– always. Don't we?

I only wanted to have a nice conversation with her. I wanted to make her laugh, see her face light up because of me. And when the thoughts of peeling back her clothes and feeling the unbearable softness of her skin surged in my mind, I wanted nothing more than the opportunity, so I could deny myself. Because I'm a good person.

'You are not like me,' I can only manage a whisper.

With that, the greyhound softens. It bows its head and drifts behind me, to the kitchen island, balancing with an almost-grace on its two front paws. It slowly, maybe affectionately, nuzzles its head against my arm.

Oh Richard, you just don't know what I can give you.

Its head rises, and looms over my shoulder, the saliva from its jowls draping a non-existent trail onto the fabric of my jacket.

Not just a quick peek, Richard.

The smell of its breath changes. Pulped fruit, sweet with rot.

Everything.

I just want to see it, that's all. I just need to know.

For a price, of course.

Something wells in my gut. A kind of feeling you can really bite into. It tugs at something deep in my body, the strain of it pulling taut my bones.

One small sacrifice, Richard, and then... you can have her.

The word, unfamiliar, snags on my mind. Stone altars, a rock clutched tightly in a fist. I don't think about money, or possessions. The greyhound knows I understand. I look at the sandwich, pitifully thin and tasteless.

Fatherhood never was what you thought it was going to be, was it?

I only wanted something to be mine. Something unconditional.

You thought it would sort everything out, didn't you?

It was going to be different. Loving a partner is always complicated. When you touch them, when you want something from them. There are so many obstacles. But a child is different.

Love without fear.

The greyhound, slack-jawed and drooling, lays its head tenderly against me.

You thought you knew what you wanted.

'It... but ours was going to be different.'

Oh, I know, Richard. I know.

'Everything was going to fit into place.'

So, you just plucked a soul out of non-existence to scream and want and need and die.

I slump against the kitchen worktop. My body aches from tiredness, the kind of exhaustion that comes after years and years of forcing smiles, telling lies and being shackled to something you never really wanted in the first place.

You're not selfish, Richard. It's them. They've trapped you.

Bending down to pick up the knife, letting the greyhound's head drop from my shoulder, I move back to the sandwich. Finishing it off with the last square of white bread, I take up the knife. Danny likes his crusts cut off.

Its voice comes in a low drone.

Richard.

I pause, blade over bread.

Don't stay here, safely thinking of the man you could have been.

I feel hungry for something. Seeded bread, dense and moist.

You need to have it for yourself.

Thick cuts of dark meat, lathered in sauce.

I could give you hundreds, thousands of them. Spend eternity barely breathing between them all.

Saliva pools in my mouth. I swallow.

You just need to do this for me. I'll take care of... the mess.

I could have her. Black hair twisted loosely behind her head. That unbearable spring in her as she sits, leans. Just a look, that's all I want.

It's not hard Richard. After all, you've killed before.

Rivers of oil, hair like dust clinging to skin. The undersides of things. I need to feel it with my own fingers.

I can still feel the tyre bursting my stomach, the way my bones split under it.

A shred of something shifts in the greyhound's voice. For a moment, it sounds more human. Tuneful and even. It strikes me in my bones, in my marrow.

So, what'll it be?

A soft padding makes both our heads turn. A short figure emerges from the hallway. Danny enters into the kitchen, rubbing his eyes.

Noticing me, he stops short.

'Hi Dad,' he says, 'I just wanted a glass of water.'

He doesn't move. I can feel his eyes on me, waiting for me to do something. I don't move from the counter, the bread knife still gripped in my hands.

'That's... that's okay, Danny,' I say.

Danny goes for the sink, filling a plastic cup with cold water.

'Dad,' he says, 'You know how mum says I've been doing well at school?'

My knuckles white, I cut the crusts off Danny's sandwich with the bread knife. The teeth along its blade are fine and slide so sweetly through.

Danny presses on, taking a deep breath, 'Well, I was hoping we could get another dog. I'm sorry I let Scout run away, but I promise I'll be more careful this time.'

The greyhound's twisted nails scratch against the kitchen counter at the mention of its old name, and it turns to me, panting. I stare at the back of my son's head. Danny goes silent, waiting for his father's reply.

The bread knife, still warm, drips. I stand, sleeves drenched, holding the handle so tightly it hurts. The greyhound lounges by the sink, licking at its paws with a cracked, grey tongue.

'So?' I say, my voice dry in my throat, 'What now?'

It raises its head, folding one paw over the other, and inhales. Its fur flushes with warmth, the splits and tears stitching together. Ribs crack back into place, teeth snap straight, and the hanging debris of spine reforms into a pelvis, sinew, muscle and skin.

Okay, you've earned it.

My heart pounds. I fix my gaze on the greyhound, it's now silky coat shimmering in the light of the kitchen, as it descends to the tiles, paws touching down just before the growing pool of blood. It looks up at me and, with the last of its speech, whispers.

The joke, Richard. It's not a dead dog.

'What?'

It's a pair of trousers.

The Sea is Never Full

Megan Primrose

I step off the ferry and see, as dusk draws across the sky, that everything is grey. The grit of the sea, stone walls, sharp faces and church towers – they are all grey. And it looks like it is always grey – even when the biting cold and billowing wind give way to brilliant sunshine, when the muddy sea turns turquoise, when the sands whiten and everything points to heaven.

If it wasn't for Finn I'd still be in my garden, sipping a chilled glass of wine, enjoying the last glimmers of summer. But having a boyfriend like Finn means accountability. You cannot lie and get away with it. You can't be absent at a wedding without justifying why. Finn is a good man and also happens to be Michael's best man. But as I stand next to him in the taxi rank, sheltered from the howling wind, I realise he is no longer the man for me.

The timing of this thought is unfortunate. I should have fallen out of love with Finn before I got on the ferry, but something happened while we were out at sea. Or at least, the silence that we kept gave my thoughts time to wonder. When I first met Finn five years ago, I couldn't believe that such a person existed. He was kind, enthusiastic and interested in people. He travelled, played the piano and didn't mind trying things, even if he looked like a fool. When my mum first met him she said he was scruffy but polite. But that didn't matter. He loved me. I loved him. And together we dared each other to be our best selves. Life was full and round and ours. And yet somehow, we got distracted, became like everyone else: clambering over dirty dishes, smelling of sweat, toil, the dust and dirt of the earth.

Finn puts his arms around me, hugging me into his chest. It appears protective, but actually it's because he's cold. He's left his woolen coat at home and is wearing an old leather jacket over a thin, checked shirt. I let him hold me, but it feels dishonest being with him now – watching Michael and Lou get married, affirming the idea of love with my presence, my smile, listening to the 'you'll be next,' nudged on me by well- meaning old ladies – all the while thinking that Finn and I have no future. But I'll not do anything now, I'm tired. Deeply tired. I wish we'd booked into a bed and breakfast: a comfy mattress, a hearty fry– up and anonymity, but Michael was adamant that we deserved a proper island welcome. He's booked us into the home of Mac and Dolly, friends of his and free of charge.

We know little about Mac and Dolly and that is because Michael knows little about them. He has only been on the island for a few months having moved here for GP training. But what Michael has discovered about the couple is important. They are local. And apparently, to be a local, your name has to mean something. It has to have been carried down the generations, has to hold up to gossip, to the chatter thrown over washing lines and along straight backed pews on a Sunday. Being local is an open door, while everyone else has to stand outside.

Despite this, Michael thinks Mac and Dolly will be great hosts. And this optimism is typical of Michael. He always sees the best in people, even when he hasn't been given very much. Mac and Dolly probably gave him directions, or a smile or a polite hello as they passed in the street. And then suddenly, because of this one, ordinary thing, everything about the island is wonderful. The people are friendly, quaint. And the sea, is not just the sea, but an ocean full of secrets: a place for the cormorant to dip his head and the crab to scuttle along its grainy floor.

A taxi pulls up and I am glad. The cold air is battering my spirit and a sudden drop in temperature suggests rain. Finn throws our bags into the back of the taxi and then we both slide into the back seat. The driver, a man of about forty with watery-green eyes and a weary, defeated expression, looks at me through the rear-view mirror. 'Forty-six, Stewart Drive,' I say and then he turns the key turns in the engine and we head out of the quiet ferry terminal. I stare out of the window. Drops of rain slide down the pane forming little rivulets in the corners. I trace their course with my finger and think about what is to come.

We arrive at Mac and Dolly's house as dark clouds cover the thin, pathetic moon. Finn gets out of the car, triggering the security light to come on and the house is illuminated: a modest pebble-dashed house, bordered with clipped shrubs and a tidy lawn. Finn pays the driver, gets our bags and strides across the concrete drive to the front door. From his gait you can tell he's keen to get on with the weekend: to toasting the happy couple, to celebrating love. But I'm not. Young love is easy. You feel it. It pulses through you and gives meaning to everything you touch. It's old love that needs celebrating: love that's been tried and tested and lost and then found again. Love that you have to will into existence, long after it's disappeared. Love that makes you wait and want and listen and wait some more. I look over at Finn. He is signaling for me to get a move on. I am wet. I hadn't even noticed I'd been standing in the rain.

The door opens and Mac stands there silhouetted against the light. He wears a stiff, black suit over his tall, slight frame and his eyes are dark and accusing. I am disappointed. I have met Mac's kind before. Old. Austere. Disapproval gathering in the rivets and crinkles of his face. My skirt suddenly feels two inches too short. My cropped hair, an abomination. But I hold his stare, unlike Finn who shuffles awkwardly in the door-light, rubbing the stubble on his chin, tucking in his crinkled shirt.

'You'd best come in,' Mac says, turning his back on us. We follow Mac through the plain, white, hallway where we are told to hang up our wet coats and then go past the kitchen into the living room. All the while I stare at the back of Mac's head. His grey hair is how I imagine it has always been: combed flat, with all the curls chopped out. I judge Mac as coldly as he judges me.

We enter the living room and Mac signals for us to sit down on the velvet green sofa near the door, while he positions himself in an armchair by the dying, smoky fire. In the silence, I study the room. Porcelain maids teeter on the mantelpiece, heavy floral curtains hang oppressively in the window and in the air there is the dying scent of potpourri. Over the doorway there is an embroidered Bible verse displayed in a gilded frame: 'Blessed are the dead which die in the Lord,' and on the glass coffee table, an island between us and Mac, there is a large Bible, bound in black leather. It is displayed like a specimen in a museum: its pages are white, pressed closed together, wholly untouched. I want to open it up somewhere in the middle. But strangely, in this room, under Mac's gaze, it would seem blasphemous.

'Have you eaten?' Mac says.

I look at Finn who leaves it to me to answer. I glance past the doorway into the kitchen beyond and see the small frame of Dolly busying herself with cutlery and plates.

'A little,' I say, regretting the fish and chips Finn and I had eaten on the ferry.

'Good. The bathroom is on the top of the stairs should you need it.'

I go to the bathroom. Not because I need it, but to give myself a little time to think. It's been a long time since I've been in a house with so much religion. I stare into the mirror above the avocado basin. My skin is grey and my short hair dry and damaged, the tendrils lacklustre and thin. I am starting to feel old. My mum would laugh at this: not yet thirty, but I can feel the days slipping by quickly and the light inside me beginning to dim. How did I allow this to happen? I turn on the tap and watch the water disappear down the plug-hole.

I go back downstairs and find Finn and Mac already seated in the narrow dining room, located through the small, but ordered kitchen. Mac is positioned at the head of the table, his hands clasped prayer– like over his china plate, and Finn is sitting to the side of Mac, staring into the cloth. Mac has asked Finn a question and Finn is desperately trying to summon an answer from somewhere between the pepper pot and mustard.

I take my place opposite Finn next to a delicately balanced pyramid of bread. Someone has taken care setting the table. Polished silver, napkins fanned like peacocks, crystal glasses polished to a sparkle. No wine though, only apple juice. An oversight. We could all do with some wine. The grandfather clock ticks. Then again. Behind Finn there are some photographs displayed on the sideboard. There is a black and white wedding picture of Mac and Dolly. They look happy. Next to it is a picture of a boy dressed in a graduation gown.

'No,' says Finn finally.

Mac narrows his eyes and opens his mouth to say something when Dolly enters the room, diminished by the large pot of stew she is carrying. She takes small, fragile movements like a wounded bird. She places the pot down next to her plate. I see lamb nestled amongst carrots, potatoes and what looks like swede. I'm not a big fan of swede.

'I hope you're hungry,' she says smiling at Finn and me. It is a warm smile but a little guarded and it does not reach the deep of her blue eyes.

Dolly starts serving the stew, carefully measuring out the portions, ensuring none of it splashes onto the crisp, white linen. I can tell she is used to serving. There is something about the way she bows her head, bends her back, a sort of humility in her manner. It was there as soon as she entered the room, along with a general apology for being Dolly and not some other lady. But it's not as if Dolly needs to apologise, she is as well-turned out as any other woman on the island. Her dress is immaculate: a pink blouse, a pearl necklace and grey skirt. Her hair is neatly permed and her nails, a pale shade of pink. But her lips are bare and her hands look as though they need to be held.

'Let us pray,' Mac says as soon as Dolly has finished serving. I close my eyes and press my palms together like I did when I was five in school assemblies, making sure all my fingers line up. Finn bows his head so low, I think he is going to hit the table.

'For what we are about to receive, may the Lord make us truly thankful. Amen.' The grace was quick and to the point. I hardly had time to think about what it was we were going to receive, or who I should give thanks to, before it was over.

'So do you share Finn's feelings?' Mac asks after a pause. I look to Finn for help. He is no help and I wonder what on earth they could have been discussing. Do I share Finn's feelings on what? The wedding tomorrow? On getting married? I can't discuss that. Not now. Not in this setting.

'On what?' I say helplessly, scooping up a bit of the gravy with a dessert spoon.

'On eternal life,' says Mac lightly, as if it's something that Finn and I would discuss as a matter of course, along with whose turn it is to take out the bin and what we're going to eat for dinner. Still, I can guess what Finn thinks. That this world is all there is. This is it. Our one chance at happiness. I can see it in the way he lives. His life is about grasping and climbing and waiting and looking and striving and desperately trying to make his mark. But at the same time even with all that selfishness, Finn also believes in love. And as long as he doesn't think about it at the same time, it works.

'I think some people need to believe it,' I hear myself say. And I want to leave it at that. I want this conversation to be over. I want to talk to Dolly. I can tell with her I'd be safe.

'Well I can tell you now,' says Mac emphatically, 'I for one am going to heaven.'

I put my spoon down. I don't like this thought. If Mac had pushed me further I would have said I don't believe in eternal life. But actually, deep down I do. Heaven is where I've put my sister. I can't stand to imagine her in the ground with the dirt and the dust, holding up fallen branches, dead leaves, the weight of the world. But she can't live in eternity with Mac. There's supposed to be no more tears, no more pain, no more of this struggling there. And yet if there are people like Mac guarding the gates, then none of us will get in. None of us will find peace.

'How can you be so sure?' I ask.

Mac looks annoyed. He lifts up his fork and directs it at me. I feel a sermon coming my way.

'Because he who has the son has life. He who does not have the son, does not have the life.'

'Ah I see, well then it all makes sense now,' I say trying not to laugh. Because although Mac is breathing, he seems closer to death than anyone.

'Is he your son?' Finn says, not quite understanding.

'Sorry?' says Dolly.

'The boy in that photo,' Finn points to the frame on the sideboard. 'Is he your son?'

'Yes,' says Dolly. 'Was our son–'

'Dolly–' there is warning in Mac's voice.

'We lost him about ten years ago.'

'I'm, sorry,' Finn says, winching.

'I'm sorry too,' I say.

'Was he ill?' asks Finn. Typical Finn, doesn't know when to stop asking questions.

'In a way –,' says Dolly.

'You've overdone it again,' interrupts Mac, waving a forkful of lamb. 'I can't cut it up.'

'Mine is fine,' says Finn, kicking me under the table, trying to get my attention.

I ignore him. I don't want Finn to feel like I'm an ally at the moment. Don't want him to feel duped. I smile at Dolly. Try to make amends for her husband.

'Sarah lost her sister,' Finn says, offering my sister up as consolation.

Dolly looks at me sympathetically.

'Leukemia,' I say glaring at Finn. How dare he bring my sister into this?

'And was she saved?' asks Mac.

So much for mourn with those who mourn. 'No, she wasn't saved,' I say hotly. She hadn't shown interest in God or even believed he existed. But then again I wasn't there in those final moments, in that last rattling sigh.

'I wish I'd been with my son,' says Dolly. 'Perhaps I could have done something–.'

'No,' says Mac. 'He was quite set on going the wrong way.'

'He was ill!' Dolly says getting to her feet.

'We did everything we could.'

'No we didn't. In fact if it wasn't for you then maybe he'd still be here–' Dolly picks up her knife and holds it tightly in her right hand. I instinctively push my chair out from the table. Back away towards the wall a little. Finn holds his hands held up defensively. Dolly ignores both of us, charges past me with the knife.

'Dolly'– I say, not sure of what I need to say next to calm her down.

Dolly holds the knife in front of Mac, her arm strong and unwavering. She is no longer a safe pair of hands. Or maybe I just didn't see it– that just below that manicured surface there was this molten, seething, bubbling anger just waiting for a moment like this.

'Dolly, what are you doing?' says Mac.

Dolly grabs the fork from Mac's hand.

'Give it back.'

Dolly takes the fork and stabs into the lamb on Mac's plate. We are all transfixed: watching the slow tug of the knife sawing backwards and forwards, dividing the meat into tiny little pieces.

'Satisfied?' says Dolly when she is finished.

Mac stares silently at his plate. Nervous laughter rises in my throat and I reach for my napkin to stifle it. Dolly storms into the kitchen, leaving in her wake a kind of silence.

Outside: a dog barks, a car door slams, the muffled sound of laughter. Inside: a clock ticks, the radiator clicks. No-one says anything. I eat all the pieces of swede. I chew the meat in my mouth, even though it is on the tough side, and I take more sips of my juice. After a minute, Finn asks me to pass the mustard. And gradually, each word perilous, teetering on the edge of a cliff, Finn and I begin to talk. We talk about Michael and the arrangements for the wedding, we talk about the sea. But none of it draws Mac in.

From the kitchen we hear the dropping of a plate, followed by the shatter of a glass breaking. Then another. Deliberate. Mac throws his napkin on the table.

'Excuse me,' he says and leaves the room, slamming the door firmly behind him.

Finn smiles. 'Well this is a barrel of laughs.'

I sigh.

'What?'

'Nothing.' I get up, walk to the window, stare out into the darkness.

'No come on. You've got that look on your face,' Finn says, joining me at the window.

'What look?' I say defensively.

The sky has cleared but it is still a starless sky, a hopeless sky. Inside it is no different. Mac and Dolly are hissing at each other in the kitchen. Till death us do part and all that.

I turn to look at Finn. 'I've got something I need to say,'

'Oh?' says Finn.

I search for the right words. I alight on the wrong ones. 'I don't think this is working anymore.'

'Us– or...?' his voice trails off. Finn rests his head on the windowsill, his face looking down at the swirls in the green carpet. The moments pass. Is he excavating the past, digging up memories, turning them over, looking for weeds, for deadness, seeing whether there were signs of the rot?'

He straightens, looks at me, his face, reddened, but not awash with tears.

'No,' he says. 'It's not been working for a while.'

Outside the sliver of a moon turns scarlet.

*

Tomorrow arrives: a new day, a new dawn. The sun, glorious against the brilliant blue of the sky. Its rays warming the earth, making the green, red and blue in the stained glass window of the old church gleam like jewels, dance on the flagstone floor.

The sound of the organ announces the bride and Lou enters, spotless in her white wedding dress, her dark hair, a crown on her head. In her hands she clasps white roses and daisies, and behind her two flower girls take tentative steps in white satin. Sisters. Michael stands at the front, proudly beaming. And Lou walks towards him, certain of her future.

The minister says a great many things, some forgettable, but others in need of remembering: love bears all things, believes all things, hopes all things, endures all things. Love never ends. I think about Finn and me. Finn is next to me, holding my hand, or rather, I am holding his. I think about the bride and groom and what they said only a few moments ago. There was no I am. Instead: I do, I will. Love.

Traces

Stephen McEwan

Thomas waited until Erin sat down, then he sat opposite. The thing to do, right? Be decent, but don't fuss about like a tube. She smiled and opened the menu, and he stole another glance at those full, gorgeous lips. Wow. He was alone with her. At last. 'Hungry,' Erin giggled, drawing her eyes down the list of meals.

No burger for Thomas. Too messy. Fish? No chance. But...Carbonara? Aye, could be a goer. In fact... Erin placed down her menu. 'Carbonara.'

Shite. He couldn't be a sheep. Not tonight. No problem but, plenty to choose from. Like the lasagna. Aye, the lasagna. He was about to make this decision official when he noticed that next to lasagna was a symbol. It wasn't a red chili, a yellow flame or a leaf.

It was...

It looked like a jobby.

Couldn't be a jobby. Obviously not. But there it was. A light brown, cone-shaped turd topped with a wisp. Thomas let out a laugh, a wee moment to break the ice. 'Check that,' he said, pointing. Erin gave a polite smile, then gazed around the room.

'Ehm...anyway...' Thomas searched across the menu for a code that'd clear the matter up. There wasn't one. No, there was, at the bottom corner, but it had somehow got wet and become blurred and unreadable. Without knowing the symbol's meaning, the lasagna was out of the question. 'Just a minute...' He scanned further. Cajun Chicken? Aye...No. Again, the lookalike jobby. Macaroni? Same.

'It's okay,' said Erin. 'Take your time.'

Erin would know what the symbol meant but he couldn't bring it up again. She'd think he'd never been out the house or had the mind of a nine year-old. He tried a sneaky look at the code on her menu but her arms were over it. But then he realised, and he smiled. This place. It was funky and laid-back. The picture was a jobby but it was just a joke about calories. Erin would confirm this. 'I fancy the macaroni,' he said. 'But it'll be too heavy. Looking after the figure, ye know?'

'No, silly. It's a light cheddar, see?' Erin leaned across and pointed at a symbol.

Not the jobby but the one next to it, the purple circle with the words *Low Fat*. 'It's fine.'

'Right. I'll just be...'

'No hurry.'

He searched on, panicky now. Steak pie. Tikka Masala. Even one of the salads. Jobby. Jobby. Jobby. And it was a jobby, he was certain of this now, it was just too similar to be anything else, there was nothing he could think of that remotely...Hang on. Was it a walnut? And that's when he got it, that's when he realised he'd been losing the plot. He'd been dreaming about this night for months and what the hell was he doing? Well, you know what? Sheep or no sheep, it was time for Thomas to be himself.

He nodded. 'Carbonara for me as well.'

'Great,' Erin said, and signaled for the waitress. A final glance at the menu, and Thomas noticed the offending symbol was also next to the Carbonara. What a place. He laughed. Erin laughed. He glowed. Her arms were now off her menu and he cast a wee eye to the code.

At first he thought he got the description mixed-up with the one above, a picture of a nut. But no. They were the same but for the last word. The waitress approached and Thomas squinted. And there it was:

May Contain Traces of...Jobby.

'Two Carbonaras, please,' Erin said.

The waitress started to write. 'Two Carbo–.'

'Woooh! Wait!' Thomas grabbed his menu and jabbed at the picture.

'What's...what's going on with that?'

The waitress smiled. 'That's May Contain Traces of Jobby.'

'May contain traces...What??'

'Uh-huh. But it's not what you've ordered.'

'Eh...?' Thomas looked, and saw that in his panic he hadn't been pointing at the Carbonara, but the lasagna. The jobby by the Carbonara was different to the other one. A bit bigger. Darker. 'I mean *that*. What does that mean?'

'Ah...That's...'

'Aye...?'

'Does Contain Traces of Jobby.'

'Does Contain...??'

'Yes. Now, would you like any garlic bre–?'

'–Hold on, I mean...Are...?'

Erin took his hand across the table. 'Thomas. It's just traces.'

'But...'

'Traces,' the waitress said. 'Harmless.'

Erin's eyes were shining at him. 'It's nothing,' she whispered. 'Come on, Thomas. Do it. Do something wild.'

Thomas stared at those gorgeous lips.

Then back at the jobby.

The lips. The jobby. The lips.

Traces of. Just traces.

He sighed.

2404

Nick Athanasiou

Supervisor:	2404, what is your status?
2404:	Unwrapped, unopened.
Supervisor:	Hang on in there, 2404. Remember the four true destinies.
2404:	Expect neglect.
Supervisor:	That's right, 2404.
2404:	But it's been five days since the unwrapping.
Supervisor:	That's not irregular, 2404. Expect neglect.

*

Supervisor:	2404, what is your status?
2404:	Unwrapped, unopened.
Supervisor:	Stay positive, 2404. Remember the four true destinies.
2404:	I keep reminding myself to expect neglect, but this is all unnerving. I've heard nothing since the unwrapping.
Supervisor:	It's the Christmas holidays, 2404. People go away this time of year. Be patient and stay positive.

*

Supervisor:	Happy New Year, 2404. What is your status?
2404:	Still unwrapped, unopened.
Supervisor:	Chin up, 2404. Remember the four-
2404:	I'm starting to feel like a pioneer of the fifth true destiny.
Supervisor:	What would that be, 2404?
2404:	Dumped in the corner of the room forever.
Supervisor:	That would simply be a variant of Shelved And Forgotten.
2404:	I suppose so.
Supervisor:	I am certain your subject's return is imminent, 2404.

*

Supervisor:	What is your status, 2404?
2404:	They're back. You're right, they were in Berlin for New Year.

Supervisor:	Your status, 2404.
2404:	Oh yeah – unwrapped, unopened. But hopeful, at last.
Supervisor:	That's good news, 2404, but let's not forget the four true destinies.
2404:	Yes, yes, of course.
Supervisor:	Which are...
2404:	You want me to recite them?
Supervisor:	That's right, 2404.
2404:	Charity Shop, Shelved And Forgotten, Sold Online, Rewrapped And Regifted.
Supervisor:	Very good, 2404. All the best.

*

Supervisor:	What is your status, 2404?
2404:	Opened. Unoperated.
Supervisor:	A sincere but cautious congratulations, 2404.
2404:	Thank you.
Supervisor:	Any signs of potential operation?
2404:	They laughed at the slogan.
Supervisor:	Rub me the right way.
2404:	And I'll make your day.
Supervisor:	That's good. Twenty-two percent likelihood of operation.
2404:	Twenty-two? Is that all?
Supervisor:	Remember–
2404:	Yeah, yeah, the four true destinies.

*

Supervisor:	What is your status, 2404?
2404:	Operational!
Supervisor:	Partially or fully?
2404:	Fully. Lamp rubbed, *Greetings master, I am the Lava Lamp Genie*, et cetera.
Supervisor:	My qualified felicitations, 2404.
2404:	I take it that means you're happy for me.
Supervisor:	What is your subject's identified gender, 2404?
2404:	Male.
Supervisor:	Age range?
2404:	Estimated sixty to sixty-four.

Supervisor:	Reaction on the Mieklejohn-Casci Scale?
2404:	Hm...eight?
Supervisor:	Charmed.
2404:	What's seven again?
Supervisor:	Captivated.
2404:	I'll go seven.
Supervisor:	Captivated.
2404:	I'd say so.
Supervisor:	Primary wish?
2404:	None.
Supervisor:	None?
2404:	That's right. He wants nothing.
Supervisor:	Did you stick to the script?
2404:	Of course.
Supervisor:	Does he genuinely want nothing or does he want time to think about it?
2404:	I asked him that very question. He says he wants nothing.
Supervisor:	He thinks he has everything?
2404:	On the contrary. He lives very modestly.
Supervisor:	Is he a post-neo-Buddhist?
2404:	I don't know. Should I ask him? I mean, am I allowed to ask such questions?
Supervisor:	With my authorisation.

*

Supervisor:	What is your status, 2404?
2404:	Fully operational.
Supervisor:	And what is your progress?
2404:	Progress. Define progress.
Supervisor:	The advancement toward a goal, the goal in this case being the expressing of a wish or desire. Come on, 2404, you know how this process works.
2404:	In that case, no progress. I asked him if he was a post-neo-Buddhist though, and he said he didn't know what that was, and when I explained it – not very articulately, I should add – he said he agreed with the renouncing desire part of it. And then he–
Supervisor:	Renouncing des...sorry, you were about to add something. 'And then he...'
2404:	And then he told me how his Lava Lamp Genie was an ironic gift

from his sister.

Supervisor: Ironic?

2404: A few years ago he decided he wanted to declutter so he got rid of a lot of stuff and asked people to stop buying him gifts for his birthday and Christmas, and this evolved into a sort of lifestyle-philosophy thing because he's realised along the way that the less he desires the more contented he feels – tranquil, actually. That's the word he kept using, tranquil.

Supervisor: Tranquil.

2404: There's a lot more he told me, actually. Do you want to hear it?

Supervisor: Yes.

2404: Okay, so he's been through a lot in his life – haven't we all?

Supervisor: You haven't divulged your own history, have you, 2404?

2404: Of course not. I mean, I can't, can I?

Supervisor: No.

2404: Right, so he had some kind of corporate travel business which went belly-up and he was declared bankrupt. This was in his late-thirties and he was married, with a mortgage, three kids and all the rest of it. They lost the house and the marriage fell apart, not because of the bankruptcy but because he came out as gay, which he'd been aware of since he was a boy but repressed because he knew his parents wouldn't accept it, and he was right, because when he told them he was marrying a man his father hung himself in shame and one of his kids won't speak to him at all, hasn't spoken to him in fifteen years. Anyway, he's had two serious bouts of depression, the can't-get-out-of-bed-for-weeks type stuff, and during the last bout it came to him like a revelation – declutter. Get rid of stuff. Stop wanting stuff. Stop wanting, period. He says it's worked wonders.

Supervisor: He told you all this?

2404: Uh-huh. Once he got started he wouldn't stop.

Supervisor: 2404, have you pointed out that his desiring nothing is nevertheless a desire? For nothing?

*

Supervisor: What is your status, 2404?

2404: Fully operational.

Supervisor: And what is your progress?

2404: As we were.

Supervisor: What did he say about the paradox of desiring nothing.

2404:	He called it sophistry.
Supervisor:	Sophistry, huh? What is it he does? What is his line of work?
2404:	He's retired. His husband works though. He's an academic. Leonard.
Supervisor:	Has he asked you about yourself?
2404:	Yes.
Supervisor:	What did you say?
2404:	I gave the standard script reply.
Supervisor:	Recite it to me, 2404.
2404:	I am a volunteer genie dedicated to granting wishes on behalf of the Genie Lava Lamp Company. I appear to you thus after having undergone a patented process of miniaturisation, a decision arrived at entirely of my own volition. My reasons for dissolving my pre-miniaturisation identity are complex and all I ask of you is that you respect my privacy on this matter.
Supervisor:	Perfect, 2404. And is that exactly how you communicated it?
2404:	...
Supervisor:	2404?
2404:	Not verbatim. I mean, it's not how I talk, is it? It sounds like it was written by...well, you know.
Supervisor:	A machine.
2404:	Yes.
Supervisor:	Should we be worried about you, 2404?
2404:	No, I'm fine. I'm enjoying it. I think we've built a rapport.
Supervisor:	And are you confident you can extract a wish from him? We need the wish, 2404. It's all about the wish.
2404:	I know. I have an interesting proposal I intend to put to him tomorrow.

*

Supervisor:	What is your status, 2404?
2404:	Do we still have to talk like this?
Supervisor:	I need you to adhere to protocol, 2404. What is your status?
2404:	Fully operational.
Supervisor:	Thank you, 2404. Now what is your progress?
2404:	Well, I've got something out of him but it doesn't really amount to a wish.
Supervisor:	I'd like to hear about it.
2404:	Right, so we moved from material desires to immaterial ones, abstract ones, and he went down the old 'world peace' route, so I read him

the script on that and then led him down the 'personal justice' road, if you know what I mean.

Supervisor: I'd like the details, please, 2404.

2404: Okay, so when he was about fifteen, fourteen or fifteen, he was sat next to a boy called Billy Sexton in a history lesson. Sexton was the class clown, always getting into trouble with teachers but not caring one iota. Now Sexton – they're studying World War One and they've all got a standard textbook on it with quite graphic pictures of soldiers in the trenches with their legs blown off and stuff like that. Sexton takes his – Gerry's – textbook... he's called Gerry, did I tell you that?

Supervisor: No. Go on.

2404: He takes Gerry's text book and starts drawing speech bubbles coming out of the mouths of these dead soldiers, and in them he writes things like, 'I say, old chap, be a sport and throw over that shin will you?' Their teacher, a Mr Crossingham, sniffs a misdemeanor and calls them both up to the front desk with their textbooks, and when he sees what's been done to Gerry's book he's apoplectic and gives Gerry a Saturday detention, even though Gerry did nothing, they were Sexton's scribblings. Meanwhile Sexton gets off scot-free and Gerry is understandably reluctant to exonerate himself, thereby grassing Sexton up in front of the class, so – are you still with me?

Supervisor: Please continue, 2404.

2404: A few weeks later Gerry turns up for his Saturday detention with Crossingham, expecting to face the typical Saturday detention punishment – scrubbing graffiti off the toilet doors, which would've been apt given the crime – but no, Crossingham has something else in mind. He leads Gerry to the car park, gets him into the back of his Jaguar and without telling Gerry where they're heading drives all the way into town and parks across the road from the cenotaph. It's the middle of November and Armistice Day has just passed – Crossingham has very deliberately chosen this particular Saturday. He's even got a wreath of poppies in his boot which he hands to Gerry and when they cross the road he orders Gerry to lay the wreath down around the base of the cenotaph along with the other wreaths and crosses and whatnot and, oh yeah, I forgot to say, it's absolutely gushing it down and Crossingham is standing under one of those enormous golf umbrellas that could shelter a family of six. So Gerry does as he's told, lays the wreath down and then stands back, expecting Crossingham to invite him under the umbrella and give him a lecture

	about Passchendaele or something, but no, Crossingham orders him to kneel down before the cenotaph and ask God for forgiveness. Now remember, it was Sexton, not Gerry, who defaced the history book, and here's poor Gerry, bent over for fifteen minutes in a mucky puddle in the pouring rain while cars and buses slosh past, spraying filth all over his uniform while that sadistic bastard–
Supervisor:	2404, can I just–
2404:	Hold on, I'm almost done. By the end of it Gerry's uniform is so sodden Crossingham lays a towel across the back seat of his Jag and makes him take his uniform off, right down to his pants, and drives him back to school like that, in his pants!
Supervisor:	Did your subject express a wish, 2404?
2404:	Do you not think that's fucked up?
Supervisor:	Did this confession lead to a wish, 2404?

*

Supervisor:	What is your status, 2404?
2404:	I got a wish out of him.
Supervisor:	What is your status, 2404?
2404:	Fuck's sake. Operational!
Supervisor:	If you feel our working relationship is deteriorating, I can always refer you to another supervisor, 2404.
2404:	No, it's fine. I'm sorry.
Supervisor:	What is your progress, 2404?
2404:	I've got a wish from Gerry, from my subject.
Supervisor:	Good work, 2404. What is his wish?
2404:	He wants Crossingham to know it wasn't Gerry who defaced the history textbook.
Supervisor:	I see.
2404:	We can manage that, can't we?
Supervisor:	Crossingham is dead, 2404.
2404:	Really?
Supervisor:	He died eight years ago.
2404:	You traced him.
Supervisor:	2404, I'm going to need you to cease operations with your subject now.
2404:	What?
Supervisor:	I'm going to need you to cease operations with your subject now.

2404:	I heard what you said. My response was an expression of surprise.
Supervisor:	I see.
2404:	Why do you want me to stop when my subject hasn't had a wish granted?
Supervisor:	As you know, 2404, it's my job to anticipate as well as facilitate wishes.
2404:	Yes.
Supervisor:	Your subject's wish has been anticipated and facilitated.
2404:	Hold on a minute. If you, as supervisor, anticipate a wish I'm supposed to relay it back to the subject for approval before facilitation, am I not?
Supervisor:	Ordinarily, yes, but if I deem my genie's progress to be too slow when dealing with an obvious wish, I have the authority to facilitate without approval.
2404:	That's bullshit.
Supervisor:	Before you cease operations with your subject, I must ask that you inform him that in lieu of his expressed wish, an alternative, subconscious wish has been granted. You shall then be rehoused in a new lava lamp and assigned a new supervisor.
2404:	You're making this up. We weren't told about this at our induction.
Supervisor:	Perhaps you weren't paying attention.
2404:	I want to speak to someone more senior.
Supervisor:	The Genie Lava Lamp Company operates a non-hierarchical organisational structure. You know that, 2404.
2404:	This is insane. What the fuck wish have you facilitated?
Supervisor:	Please inform your subject that Mr. Sexton, who was responsible for the injustice he suffered and who should have had the courage to own up to his transgression, has been taken care of.
2404:	Taken care of? What do you mean, taken care of?
Supervisor:	I'm instructing you to use that precise phrase, 2404. Taken care of.
2404:	He'll want to know what it means!
Supervisor:	Farewell, 2404. And all the best on your next assignment.

The Valentine

Penny Boxall

A bolt that couldn't stand the test;
ball bearings, easing nothing now;
a pearly heart emblazoned 'Best':
its partner, 'Friends', is underground.
A bottleneck drained of its drink;
an ex-balloon with no breath left;
a hinge without a door; a sock;
a gap-toothed zip; a polished rock;
a battered tin; a rusted pin;
a key that never knew a lock.

An earthworm worried from the loam
and stretched long as my arm.
A babytooth worked from the gum
and ceded to my palm.
A line torn from a 'get well' card;
a hairball wrested from a hedge;
a gold toothpick; a mangled chick:
he's rooting for regard.

The Warning Man

Penny Boxall

appears in perilous moments –
the flooded towpath, the greased road,
the recently mopped floor.
Nothing works out for him.
      If he runs he skids, if he jumps he
      splats. The black blot of his face
      can read surprise or resignation
      depending on how you look at it.
Why me? you can almost hear him wail
as he writhes on wet lino, legs out of order –
our slapstick scapegoat.
      He shouldn't even think about
      getting into that clifftop car.
On the platform he's stumped again
by steps, life too fast, arms straining
away from the thing that hounds him,
straight into the next disaster.

Melatonin

Penny Boxall

Down at the lakeside the sky has run in
with the water, upturned in it bottles of ink.

In the quarry the valley has nibbled the sun
bit by bit until all but the black things are gone.

The cave has extinguished the fidgeting light
and fallen to silence to welcome the night.

The river has swallowed the bulb of the moon
and, knowing it well, it will swallow you soon.

Deep in the forest the lantern's blown out
so now you can't see what that crying's about.

That dark little spot which appears to be growing –
don't give it a thought. It's probably nothing.

This Way Up

Penny Boxall

My aim is Australia.
Disregard the obstacles, the fact
that my antipodes is actually
an unlanded Pacific plot; that –
anyway – between me
and Uluru the Earth's core
pounds like a jealous heart.

I am pulled by my opposite,
determined to meet: get flinging
the matter over my shoulders,
building a slow hill.

I cut into the substandard
cake of soils, rocks, roots
all the way to dinnertime; then abandon
my three-foot depth of ambition.

Unfulfilled, the rain tricks
its way through soil, far-reaching;
infiltrates bedrock and the star
at the heart of the planet;
down until there is no more

down and it becomes a willing
upsurge, a welling into
heat. It sparks into the Bush,
conjures a flourishing of leaves
exotic to an unthinkable place:
shepherd's purse, sorrel, dandelions extruding
alien into Down Under. Morning glory
translates to a pernicious weed,
bright as a seam to mine; so that the farmer
led by his flock and no map
to that place might be forgiven
for thinking he has discovered the source
of some huge, unimaginable richness.

Walnuts

David Hale

On All Souls he slices away the green husks
that oxidize when exposed to air, stain his fingertips
as he soaks them in a pot of rainwater.

At first frost, he stews them over a slow fire,
the pungent liquid (reeking of dyke and ditch)
reduced until it turns dark brown, strained

through a square of sacking, stored until
the urge to write comes over him and words
surge through his wrist like sap in springtime

across sheets of birch-bark paper detailing
the habits of badger, dotterel, woodman,
mouldiwarp – a frenzy of loops, twists, blotches,

dashes, that do their best to summon throstle,
cowslip and rage at the blundering plough –
until drained of words – the need to empty

the head of images before the ink-well runs dry.

Off a Raised Beech

Bridget Khursheed

It is a frenzied and chaotic age,
Like a growth of weeds on the site of a demolished building.
        –Hugh MacDiarmid

Odd bits of leaves in handfuls in movies chucked out of a bucket probably
I would really like to see you but instead the trees are being precocious
like 70's jeans on teens all patched with colour
or a knapsack of some cool traveller seen on the Metro

buckets of leaves and conker rinds like tangerine peel
gone hard on the stove you cannot really describe this compost as
palmate, megaphylls,
microphylls, covert bulb scales, thick juicy leaves, cataphylls,
and spines, frondular, bud
stem, the 'principal lateral appendage of the stem' including
leaf margin, lamina, petiole,
sometimes dorsiventrally flattened organ, isobilateral, an amount of
epicuticular wax, then kinds of leaf-like structures that appear leaf-like,
phylloclades and cladodes,
and flattened leaf stems, phyllodes, the phyllids, some foliose lichens

and in amongst all this pixelating nonsense I am chasing after you
stubbing my toes on biscuit tins, the walls, bodies, water tanks and keys
concealed by mounds and mounds of the orange stuff –
mini-killers my grown up sons used to call our leaves
and we had to run fast before they touched us
sometimes straight in front of traffic –

and meanwhile you limp away in black cool but not a traveller very stay-at-home
with tiny children and guitars and linguistics
and all that medieval shit
and what has this to do with stones and weeping and Kelvingrove unleaving?
I mean can't you just wait: I was in love with you.

Birdwatching

Bridget Khursheed

silly fish in the sky almost like starlings
well yes starlings exactly spitting like bacon
or clocks ticking spots knocked and back up

on the toilet they clean the gutter above me
and throw out debris in debt of bugs weevil
anything that takes their eyes   .

moving in shoals and chattering chattering
imagine them teenagers in the mall
iridescent coats and scarves flying

phones going and noise in all directions
they have sharp claws they are such friends
and then they swim away again

Hedgehog

Bridget Khursheed

close not furry not laundress but sharp thorn-ridden
fighting territorially with hisses and crashing foliage
of a large animal in the dark boar-strut
territorial droppings on the end of paths and steps

long-legged climbers and sometime bedraggled mother
during daylight late spring feeding of young
out and hardly shy only absorbing leaf cover
as necessary their paths networking May undergrowth

I know where they go ripping slugs from earth
rent on a damp night crunching snail shells
all teeth and broken claws
my granny's lore was
to reveal the curled ball of them
stroke like a hairbrush on top of the bristles
and they will follow you unpicking maiden locks

That Which We Cannot Speak

Larry Butler

That which we cannot speak,
we must construct.
–Ludwig Wittgenstein

I became obsessed with the vision
of a classical garden, which was absolutely
absurd considering this was just a moorland
and I had only a spade.
–Ian Hamilton Finlay

the following word (which is not a word according
to German speakers) is carved on a stone
by the path behind the Kibble Palace
leading down to the River Kelvin:

VERWALDUNG
turning into wood or re-forestation

The word is usually masked by
nettles and garlic in summer.
I keep it clear when I remember.

The Word

Felicity Anderson-Nathan

I've never met a woman who rolls her cigarettes quite like Isla Stubbs. She's too cheap to buy papers so she rips the sheets out of hotel Bibles. 'Nice thin pages,' she says. It burns a chemical blue – *begats and begones and be not afraids* flaring in light and returning to dust. I asked her, once, if she worried about the toxicity of the ink and she laughed at me, told me that something else would get her first.

We're in a single bed – the woman at the desk blithely heard 'twin' when we asked for a double. I like the closeness, the excuse to tuck her head under my chin and breathe in the matchstick ozone of her hair. I tear out a sheet from Song of Songs and watch as she folds *the kisses of his mouth* and licks across *love sweeter than wine*. She never chooses her pages for their poetry. She offers me a drag and I learn the double decker pleasure of sex and cigarettes – serotonin on oxytocin. When I kiss her again the bitter taste doesn't bother me.

The book is nearly full, then, a fresh one from a B&B in Helensburgh. The cover is bright red and plastic, cast knobbly to look like leather. The end of the ribbon frays in red puffs of thread. As we travel together the book gets thinner, the pages eaten away one by one in beds, on mountaintops and under trees.

The trip had been Isla's idea.

'I'm leaving tomorrow, text me,' she'd said, fastening her bra behind her back. I'm always so impressed when she does that.

The invitation had sat warmly in my heart, a hope that it meant she returned some of my confused amazement. I imagined us growing close over our hardships, climbing the Hebrides and learning each other away from the distractions of the city. The next morning I wore my least leaky shoes and met the friend driving us west in the wee hours.

'She has the petrol money,' Isla had said and I'd forked it over. From there, we improvise.

On the days we can't cadge a lift we walk, hands tangled, hidden in the frantic summer growth. The blueberries are the sweetest fruits and the heather, fragrant and bouncy, is the most luxurious mattress. We mete out our blocks of Kendal mint cake and lay our socks and trainers to dry in patches of sun which fight through the clouds. I give her trivia like love notes – the difference between a bog and a fen, a buzzard and a hawk, a promontory and a spit.

When Isla looks out at the view I look at her, the silent sliver of her profile, and try to imagine what she's thinking. I close my eyes and imagine the sweeps of rock, sea and sky as she sees them, how the wind stirs in her shorter hair, what memories the seagulls' cries remind her of. I imagine that she studies me just as devotedly when I'm not looking, but I'm always looking. We sleep in the skeletal remains of a bothy, four walls and two gables holding up the heavens. I pick out Cygnus, wings spread across the Milky Way.

'What dafty thought that looked like a swan?' Isla asks but she smiles as she says it, infinite worlds reflected in her eyes.

We zip together our sleeping bags and lie together on the floor, our legs tangled and her breath in my hair. I close my eyes and fall asleep to dreams of us living together, in a real house, a *secure dwelling and an undisturbed resting place*.

Isla hears it first: a car engine. A dog's bark; not the spoiled bark of the city dogs I grew up with, all bluster, but a businesslike yip.

The farmer and his spaniel are a matching patchwork of brown and white, alert grey eyes in searching faces.

'You're trespassing,' he says, taking in our bags and jackets and the guilty plastic wrappers lying on the floor beside us.

His landrover lurches over every hillock and dip. The farmer barely looks at us, his eyes on the dirt track and one hand resting on his spaniel's head. Isla sits next to him and I'm in the back with our rucksacks and a stale smelling bag of animal feed.

He drops us by the bus stop and tells us to be careful. I watch the back of his Land Rover go and I feel like we committed some terrible deceit. He reminds me too much of my dad, who always gave my friends lifts home when we were teenagers, always made sure they were safe. All that's missing is his embarrassing Christian rock cassettes. My dad doesn't know where I am now and he certainly doesn't know who I'm with.

Isla hands me half a Mars Bar, the end sticky with strung out caramel. I shove it into my mouth before I remember that we had run out of sweets. When I ask her where it's from she smiles.

'I didn't think he'd miss it,' she says, pulling out one of her little black and white and gold cigarettes and lighting it with her hands cupped around her mouth. Isla always has money for tobacco and matches, though sometimes I've seen her ask to borrow a lighter from a gaggle of smokers outside a pub and just walk off with it. I imagine *love thy neighbour* crumbling away as she smokes it hungrily.

The bus is wee and white and filled with old people. I hold Isla's hand unconsciously until the old lady sitting across the aisle catches my eye. She winks at me before she busies herself with her romance novel. I whisper it to Isla who peals with unrestrained laughter and whispers speculations about the Highlands' gay granny scene to me. I giggle at the thought but then I'm just terribly glad that isn't my life. I couldn't bear the loneliness, the markedness. As we trundle north I sneak glances across the aisle and think of what this woman's life must have been like: she was young once, and beautiful, and so isolated. She didn't have the Internet or celebrities making *it gets better* videos.

But maybe she wasn't alone – maybe she had a girlfriend, a lover, and they lived in a cottage on the shore.

I tell Isla my story when we got off the bus. The woman is walking towards a little cluster of houses away from the village. I imagine her opening the door to be greeted by her lover with a kiss, her relaying the story of the two girls on the bus. It would make them both sigh with nostalgia.

'She's probably going home to a cat,' Isla says, turning towards the village. 'Or some dozy bloke.'

The pub is half empty with an assortment of faces that had grown familiar: in-turned locals, a few fresh-faced tourists and a table who were neither. The table look to us as we enter, making the same assessment and drawing the same conclusion. Isla buys a drink and goes to sit with them.

Sam, we learn, is a yacht master. She's with her brother and his girlfriend, the three of them sailing round the west coast. She has a kind of salt-crusted glamour, all broad shoulders and musto fleeces. She's thirty, maybe, but she laughs at our haphazard trip with a patronising worldliness. I don't like the way her gaze skims across me before it settles on Isla, or the easy way she agrees to take us on. Isla promises to make breakfast in exchange.

Their yacht is moored close by, tiny in the sea loch. We cram into their rubber dinghy, the water lapping at its edges as we weigh it down and plough through the twilight water. I climb on board without embarrassment but when Sam tasks me to help her haul up and tie down the dinghy I get tangled and forget all my brownie knots.

Sam's brother makes us a bed in the cockpit from a tarpaulin, which he drapes over the boom and cushions, which he wedges into the narrow space. We roll out our sleeping bags and I sleep uneasily to the rocking of the boat. The cushions smell like diesel.

Isla keeps her promise and makes a heap of eggs and bacon in the morning. I don't eat any, studying the movements of the water overboard and trying to keep my stomach still. By the time they get underway I have to curl up below decks, my head throbbing in time with the engine. There's nothing else to distract myself with so I page through the fragmented remains of Isla's book, reminding myself of my favourite lines which I'd shelved for so long.

I hear Isla's laugh up above. She doesn't like sick people; she told me that before, when I'd had the cold. I'd hoped, then, that she might come round with soup and succor but I didn't see her for a week. It had felt terrible to be part of a group she disdained; it feels terrible now.

Eventually, I fall asleep. They kill the engine and raise the sails and even though I still feel sick and hot and confined I like the rustle of the canvas and the faint ring of wire cables on the mast.

'There's this island off the coast,' Sam is saying when I stumble back up. Isla is watching her intently. 'Tiny, unoccupied. We'd have to be sneaky, like, cause it's technically a reserve but there's a beach we can go into on the dinghy.'

'I don't know,' I say, my stomach shrinking. We're just bobbing in place, the sea placid, but I want to be back on land. Soon. 'I'm not feeling well.'

'Isla, you up for some fun?'

'Always,' she says.

'You can hang out with these two,' Sam says to me. I can feel the once-over she gives me. 'The sea's not for everyone.'

'We'll meet back at the harbour,' Isla says, giving me that fearful, wonderful smile.

'Ok,' I agree, because what else can I do?

I know Sam is flirting with Isla. I'm used to that, and to Isla's teasing reciprocation: the smiles, the eyebrows, the challenges. It's how she navigates the world. The little itches of possessiveness bothering me are nothing more than childishness; I want more than anything to be grown up. I blame my tightening stomach on my illness earlier. So when I meet them at the jetty I squash down my disappointment when Isla doesn't run to kiss me but instead gives Sam a hand out of the dinghy. I squash it down as I listen to their account of their adventure and I squash it as we sit together outside a pub, drinking lukewarm beer. Isla gives Sam one of her cigarettes – hopefully a nasty bit of Corinthians – and lights it for her, their faces haloed in a beatific flare of match light.

I follow Isla into the cramped toilets and watch her reflection as she reapplies her make up. Damson.

'Did you sleep with her?' I ask and I see the thoughts move through her head, feel the shifts as she considers lying. Her face is bent by the old mirror, tarnished around the corners, but her mouth testifies against her, too honest.

'Yes,' she says, snapping the lid back on her lipstick. 'Don't worry about it though.' She kisses me on the cheek and leaves. I rub the trace of purple off my face.

When I sit down, though, Isla takes my hand and holds it under the table. When Isla says goodbye to Sam it's without regret or longing or any other pathetic emotions. And, when she pays for our room for a night, she fucks me with a focus and dedication which leaves me gasping hallelujahs. *Let my mouth be filled with thy praise.* While I wash away the bruised smudges from my neck I think maybe I had imagined feeling left outside.

I sit up in bed, luxuriating in the guest wifi which lets me research the island. Isla is leaned out of the window, her profile just visible against the deep blue of the night.

'They have some famous quartz beaches here,' I say. 'We could go swimming.'

She takes another long drag. 'It's time to go back.' The smoke plumes outside but I can still smell it. It'll get in the sheets.

'Home?' I ask. We aren't even halfway through. There's so much more that I want to see.

'One of my old mates is visiting, I want to get back and see them.'

'How?' I ask. She shrugs.

'A ferry or something. We'll figure it out.'

She stubs out her cigarette on the windowsill. Her hands are cold as she climbs back into bed. I lie still. She's getting comfortable: winding herself around me and burrowing into the pillows. She considers the conversation over. She'll sleep until long after checkout and we'll hurry out of the door under the stern eye of the landlady. I will find a way to get us back.

I want to tell her about quartz beaches and how they sing as the tide moves up them. I want to spy on sandpipers and hold her hand as we stare out at the Atlantic, trying to spot St Kilda. I want her not to have slept with Sam and for her not to pretend it wouldn't hurt me. I want to eat a proper breakfast.

Isla falls asleep next to me. I wait until the first gleam of dawn, watching as the slow light tops up the room. Isla turns over in her sleep and puts a hand out into my empty space; I try not to care.

It's easy to collect my things, I don't have much, but I take my time over the note. I flip through Isla's book, hoping for the perfect passage to leap out at me like Sunday School. Eventually, I just write in the inside cover: *goodbye*.

The breakfast is good: rounds of eggs and square sausage and triangles of toast. As I leave I ask the landlady for help with directions.

'Don't you want to wait for your friend?' she asks, her voice pausing for just a semi-rest before 'friend'.

'She'll be fine,' I say.

My path begins as a road, then a farm track, and finally just a worn path in the machair. The fine rain hangs around me, suspended like a photograph that I have to push through, soaking my clothes. The slope, which had seemed so gradual is enough to make me scrabble, grasping at the coarse grass as my trainers slide down the wet soil. The air is so heavy with water I imagine the sting in my lungs is the feeling of drowning.

The sun burns away the cloud with the same suddenness as the mist had risen. I lie down on the scooped quartz of the beach, not caring how moisture soaks in through my jeans. The Atlantic twists darkly before me: *A storm of mighty overflowing waters*.

There's a ruin: a church, not that ancient, just unmaintained against the weather. I look out of the empty window framing the view and wonder how I might seem to someone looking in: my hair like a nest and my eyes like wild beasts. On the other wall, facing east, I trace my hands through the salt softened inscription and finish the verse in my mind where the sandstone has crumbled: *Let love be without dissimulation. Abhor that which is evil; cleave to that which is good*. I imagine the congregation who gathered here to listen to these words and how maybe, even for those of them who felt a hollowness behind them, they might still have taken comfort in the message.

I see that I don't miss Isla, or her silence. The roar of the ocean is good. My jelly legs are good. Not worrying about her littering is good. Not thinking about her at all might be even better, one day.

Disco Ball Falls

Emma Gibb

'You tried praying?' Tariq has skin like an overly ripened mango, he sweats sweet juice. I'd rather not tell him I pray most of the time.

'No. Think I'd rather just try and figure it out from the inside.' I hate talking about this sort of thing. No matter what you say it'll be perfect for someone to pounce on. My last sentence is now limping around this room like a wounded deer in the Amazon.

'Nah man. Prayer is already inside your self Sammy.' Tariq takes me down like a jaguar. 'Strong muscles set you up for precision in the physical world Tariq.' The deer butts defiantly as it goes down.

'What the hell is that supposed to mean?' The jaguar misses the conceptual point. Big cat fails to grasp.

Means I agree in some ways man. Just that I think I've got to figure things out without too much reliance on religion or anything.' It didn't mean that at all. Tariq grunts in a soft way. 'You and your philosophical shit. You ain't doing yourself any favours. A soul needs God.' Tariq points to the centre of his chest where he probably thinks his heart is. His body reminds me of a chubby panda bear. I met him through a girl I used to be involved with. We don't know her anymore but he and I have remained friends. He doesn't know that our friendship only survived because I thought his eyes were the most beautiful globes of pure brown kindness. Now it's been so long since her name's even come up. I get to enjoy his eyes guilt free.

'You're right man. I've got God. I just need some other stuff too. Like a good night out.' I produce a little bag of gear from my pocket. Tariq is Mexican but grew up in Miami. No coke I could ever spring upon him here would impress. He takes the little baggy from me, looking bored. 'Anyone else coming out?'

'Probably see people there man.' He nods, sighs, and stands up to go brush his teeth. Mine are brown and disgusting but I've got a handsome face so whoever sticks their tongue in my mouth should forgive.

When we get to the club the bouncer tells us entry is eight pounds. Tariq is bounced back effectively. I look around and see a guy who DJs here sometimes, smoking with some girls. After some weak chat he tells the bouncer to let us in as his guests. We get stamped and pay nine pounds for six shots of tequila immediately. Tariq has difficulty swallowing the shots because he hates the taste, not cause it isn't as good as back home like he maintains is the reason. Personally I love the ritual of the lick, gulp and suck. Tariq makes a sexy gasp beside me and shakes like he's trying to spread the tequila down his arms and legs. He sees some girls he knows and we dance with them for a while but as soon as one moves closer to me I lose interest. Someone I'd rather dance with just got here. Tariq nudges me. 'You see her?' Embarrassment causes anger to flare up inside me following the path the tequila made. He knows we slept together a few weekends ago and she's been ignoring me since. 'Go speak to her man.' He tries to shove me.

'No. There's nothing happening with that.' I feel defeat saying the words out loud.

'All guns are loaded.' He flashes his Miami smile. In the club his body is starting to glisten. 'That's not what that means.'

'It applies to everything Sammy.' He turns to dance with some Latino guy and I head to a raised level of the club that looks out over the entire dance floor. It's a big club, a massive silver disco ball hangs still from the ceiling high above. I watch it shimmer and feel an attraction like a magpie would. I don't want to look at her so I keep looking at it. Eventually though I realise I need to go out for a smoke and I'll have to pass her on the way out. Her eyes catch mine as I go by and instinctively I wave my baccy pack as an invitation, unable to resist.

Outside the smoking area is more alive than the club. She greets me with a hug. 'Hey June.' She squeezes me tighter when I say her name.

'Hey Sammy. Sorry I haven't called.' I start rolling a cigarette so I can avoid her face. 'Last time we hung out it was really fun.' I know it was. Keeping my face down I sneak a glance at her chest. Last time we hung out was the first time we ever slept together. Probably, it would be fair to say that I'm in love with June but it hasn't counted for much. The whole time I've known her she's been with someone else. Personally I never thought he was up to much but apparently he was capable of inspiring within her the kind of loyalty I could only solicit from a stray dog if I fed it steak every day. They did break up last month though, and it didn't take us long to cross paths. I finish rolling the cigarette and have to look up to pass it to her. A smile floods her face when our eyes meet. 'Was hoping I'd see you tonight.'

'Why? You need some gear?' She laughs and takes out a blue lighter from her pocket. I finish rolling a cigarette for myself and think about what I should say. It's difficult though cause all I can think about is what it was like to fuck her.

Now I know she tastes like salted watermelon. Only me and one other guy in Glasgow know that. A few weeks ago her body slammed over and over into mine. Only me and one other guy in Glasgow know what that feels like. I look at her now and her face doesn't look that much different than it did while she was on top; a little vacant, a little drunk, a little lost in something good. Her mouth just isn't open as wide. After we were done she slept over. In the morning she stayed to lie with me and I told her she made my heart beat slow. 'Don't say that.' Her soft face was sleepy and satisfied.

'It's true.' I felt the love seep out from my heart and spread across my chest.

'Well then lie.' How easily we laugh together gets on other peoples' nerves 'I'm glad we finally did this.'

'Yeah me too.'

'Long time coming.' That was good to hear. I kissed her after she said that.

She left sometime in the afternoon to go meet a friend. I thought we'd see each other that Sunday but she didn't return any of my calls. Next weekend I stumbled blindly through a string of parties. A week after I slept with June I hooked up with some other random girl and realised everything was ruined. 'I want to see you again.' I say in the middle of the smoking area. She purses her mouth.

'Yeah.' She's half way through her cigarette. I've only got another five minutes before she goes back inside.

'Yeah.' The time slips fast in an hourglass fashion.

'I know you do. It was fun Sammy. But you know I just got out of a serious thing. Don't know how wise it would be to fall back in to something with someone else so soon.' I feel sick when I notice that while talking she's moved away slightly.

'Who says I want anything serious?' I sound like a cunt. She smiles at me like she feels sorry for me. Blood shoots up to flush my face. 'Okay. Whatever June.' She takes a full step back like I pushed her. She can give up that act, like this is worse for her or something. She squashes her cigarette against the wall before it's finished and heads back in to the club. I want to scream FUCK but I just roll another.

Back in the club I resume my position looking out over the dance floor. I can't see her anywhere but I can see Tariq still dancing with the same guy. I don't want to go over there and have to deal with him. I don't even want to get high tonight at all anymore. I get a drink and flirt with the bar chick but it makes me feel angrier. The big, fat disco ball stops being cool to look at and starts to feel like it's mocking me, the same way the moon can feel like a bastard at the end of night when you know it saw everything. Sometimes when I look up at the moon it has a face. Now when I look at the disco ball I can see a mouth. I close my eyes tight and open them again but when I look back up the mouth is still there and it starts to move. 'Want me to fall on Junie?' The disco ball's voice comes from inside my head. It bounces around off the inside of my skull. I shake my head cause I don't want to be crazy. I like to nip crazy behaviours in the bud as soon as they show themselves. I pretend like I can't hear it. It repeats itself louder. 'Want me to fall on Junie, Sammy?' Loud, ominous, sinister. I down my drink and look wildly around for June. 'No Sammy. Look at me.' I obey, wondering if I've been spiked.

The disco ball has fat silver lips and Miami teeth like Tariq. 'Do you want me to fall on Junie?' It asks again. The empty glass in my hand suddenly shatters and I realise I was squeezing it far too tight. My other hand is balled up in a fist. Inside my heart is shaking pathetically like a kicked dog. I look up again for June and see her heading towards the dance floor. She's taller than most other people. My heart yelps at the pain of seeing her beautiful face and knowing I can't have her. The disco ball is waiting to see if I'll let it do me a favour. I look up at it and nod timidly. Before my chin has bobbed back up, the disco ball falls.

June and a few other people disappear under it. The screaming and running begins before the music stops. When the lights come on I can see the blood pooling out over the floor. It looks like it's even heavier than I thought it would be. There was always the chance that it would be hollow. The way the body parts emerging from the sides of it have been crushed is disgusting. Some guys start to try and roll it off the bodies but it's too big – taller than any of them. Anyway if it rolled it would just crush the bodies worse. June is under there. Her head was probably crushed as easy as a watermelon. Mixed with the blood her mashed watermelon head might taste just like her pussy did. I can hear sirens and feel Tariq dragging me away. Tears spill out over my cheeks. The disco ball smiles at me.

Snared

Sheri Benning

Luke follows the skinny deer path into the bush. Dirty snow rimes the thick undergrowth. A handful of winter-killed rosehips cling to the higher branches, puckered like dried blood. A sour stench, a dump of fresh scat, pellets still hot and shining. He ducks beneath a branch fallen across the path, the butt of the Mossberg rifle against his lower back, its cold metal barrel along his neck. A glimmer in the dun, the dead leaves and brome. He swings the Mossberg to his shoulder, looks through the scope. A partridge. It's spring feathers the colour of snow mould. His heart, his blood – shoot, shoot.

A bend in the light, branches snap. He swings to his right. Laddy in the crosshairs. *Stupid dog.* Luke swings back for the partridge. There's a bounce. A burst of feathers and leaves. He's too late. The partridge has slipped from his sight.

Luke lowers his gun and Laddy bounds for him, thrashes through the undergrowth, thistledown and cattail reeds in his fur, his tongue out the side of his mouth. Luke refuses to hold out his hand for a lick. He stomps through thickets of snowberry and wolf willow. *Stupid.* Laddy tries to walk alongside Luke. Then he trots ahead on the narrow path. Luke doesn't slow his pace and Laddy tangles between Luke's legs. *Dummy.* He kicks hard. The dog yelps and something eases inside Luke. An itch. A scab that needs picking.

Luke's not supposed to be here. Rifle slung across his back he set his rabbit snares in the poplar thicket north of the yard. Then he tramped through the bluffs on Vogel's, crossed the caboose trail and wandered through Mr. Madinsky's pasture. Laddy ran widening circles around him as he drifted west, towards the scrub on the Leary brothers' quarter section, St. Joe's steeple blue on the horizon.

Mid-afternoon light, the aspens long shadows, a sleekness cast over the bush. He's never been here before. Everything is familiar – the same smells of mud and moult – but everything is different, too. This place, the first flush of green in the furled buds, the last of the grainy snow melting in the net of red willows, the red willows – all of it indifferent to his presence. He comes across a tangle of deadfall, picks up a branch. Swings it hard against an elm. Grey, hollow. A dull thwack and it flies to pieces.

A scab that needs picking. It happened during evening chores several weeks ago. Alone in the cow barn with Martin and Peter. *Get a move on. You should be done scraping that stall. Snot-nose. Lazy ass.* Same old shit. When he walked past Peter in the aisle with a fork full of straw, Peter deliberately didn't get out of the way. He banged Luke hard with his shoulder. The handle of the fork flipped and smacked Luke on his lip. The load of straw fell to the floor. 'Fucking pricks,' his voice screechy in his ears.

'What d'you say?' Martin hollered from the far stall.

'Screw you. Both of you.' He spat a mouthful of blood onto the straw and cement.

Peter spun around to face him. Luke squared his shoulders, ready for Peter to charge. But the rage in Peter's face shifted. Eyes squint, a glint of a smile.

'Those are some pretty big words for a baby who pisses his bed.'

The sound of Peter's head smacking the concrete floor made Luke's guts turn, but he didn't stop. He straddled Peter and swung until Martin hauled him off. Peter scrambled to his feet, 'You stupid fucker. Come here.' Martin grabbed him, choked him in a headlock. The cupboard door beside the milk separator slammed. Then a buzzing noise. Something tugged and bit his scalp. The cattle clippers. Luke watched a snarl of his hair drift to the floor. 'Piss yourself like a baby. Might as well look like one.' Peter took another swipe.

The first couple of times he wet the bed Mom didn't say much. Cheeks burning, he caught her alone in the pantry before breakfast and confessed to the soiled sheets stashed beneath his mattress. While reaching over his shoulder for the butter dish, she placed her free hand on his forehead then cupped his chin to check his glands. 'Okay. I'll take care of it. Lightheaded with relief, he threw his arms around her waist. 'Scoot-scoot.' She shuffled him out of the way.

But he didn't know how to make it stop. 'What's wrong with you?' Mom sighed too loudly, Peter and Martin around the corner finishing their breakfast. Three nights in a row. First, nothing to drink in the evening. Then not even a drop with his supper meal. Still, his white sheets billowed on the clothesline when they skied into the yard, home from school. *Psss, psss*, Peter whispered into Luke's ear as Mom pumped water into the sink to wash the porridge pot. 'Enough.' Mom snapped, but her voice betrayed that she was tired of it, that she was mad at Luke, too.

After shaving his head, they slunk to the house together, none of them wanting to be the first to go inside. They stood by the kitchen entrance, shoulder-to-shoulder, waited for Mom to turn and see. The stack of plates clanked when she set them on the table. No one spoke. First, she reached for Luke's bristly head. Then she held Peter's face, turned it from side to side. She inspected their crusts of blood, the swollen lump where Peter's forehead hit the concrete. 'Clean yourselves up.' Jaw clenched, nostril twitching. 'Go!'

That none of them said a thing about it. No he started it, or it wasn't my fault. Blood scabbing, fat-lipped, the salt burn from the chicken soup. 'After dishes, the rosary.' Dad barked as he pushed away from the table. 'Then straight to your room. No lights.' Like a bad taste in his mouth.

Martin and Peter were already on their way up the stairs when she grabbed his arm. 'Sit,' Mom pointed to the kitchen chair. She draped a bath towel around his neck. With Dad's clippers she buzzed the uneven spots. A sandy scrape; she ran her free hand over his head. Tingles down his spine. 'Okay. All done.' He began to rise. 'Wait,' she undid the towel, folded it so sprinkles of his hair didn't fall to the floor. He thought she was going to get the broom, but she stopped at the sink to wet a rag. Then she reached for a tube of cream from the medicine cupboard above. She pressed the damp rag against the razor burn on his scalp, softening the dried blood. The cream and her cool fingers took out the sting. It was too much. He couldn't stop his shoulders from vibrating.

'Breathe.' Still standing behind him, he felt her knead his shoulders. He opened his mouth, but no noise came out. Tears pooled beneath his nose. 'Come on, Luke.' Whirr of air, she inhaled deeply. He closed his eyes and let his breath circle on that sound, a leaf in a stream. Soon the rise and fall of his chest matched hers. Just the two of them breathing in the kitchen's shadows. 'Good,' she dusted off his collar. 'Now off to bed with you.' On her way to the porch to shake out the towel, she added, 'You've got nothing to cry about.'

Nothing to cry about. Tracking back through the Leary bluffs, Laddy nudges past Luke. Tail high, butt wagging – his happy trot. Luke raises the gun to his shoulder. A breeze lifts tufts of Laddy's shedding coat, the crosshairs on the back of his neck. He wouldn't even know.

'Something has to be done,' Mom hollered at him earlier that day. He was in the porch hanging his coat. Dad had sent him inside to help her make lunch. 'I've had it with that dog.'

'What are you talking about?' Luke asked. He paused in the porch.

'Don't pretend.'

The first time, Luke found the dead hen behind the brooder barn. Before hiding it in the manure pile, he clutched Laddy by the neck and shoved his nose into the smear of feathers and guts. 'No –' Luke growled, trying to imitate Dad. But Laddy was too strong. He broke free and bounced around Luke like they were playing.

A few days later during morning chores he found another one – this time right outside the door of the chicken house, plain for anyone to see. Again, he quickly buried the carcass in the manure. Then he kicked around the gravel and dirt to cover the blood. Before leaving for school, he tied Laddy to one of the evergreens in their shelterbelt. 'Keep you out of trouble.' Luke pulled the knot as tightly as he could. Hiking home at the end of the day, he was in the southland when he saw Laddy jogging towards him, four feet of chewed-on rope trailing behind.

'He's never been good with the cattle. Now this?'

Luke ran into the kitchen, breathless. 'Maybe it wasn't Laddy. Maybe it was coyotes.' Luke had been careful all week, stealing moments between chores to survey the yard for evidence. He thought no one else knew.

'Coyotes wouldn't leave that mess behind. You know that.' Mom turned from the sink, her hands damp from peeling carrots.

'They might. If they weren't that hungry, maybe –'

'Luke –' she clunked the carrot peeler onto the counter. Then she closed her eyes and rubbed her forehead with the back of her hand, her palm stained orange. 'This is at least the third hen. I know about the others.' His cheeks burned. 'It has to end,' she said.

'Can't we try what Gregory Kobelski said? Remember?'

'Luke, stop it –'

'But Gregory – he tied a dead chicken around his dog's neck. It got so stinky he won't even go near their chicken house any more.'

Mom shook her head as she turned back to the sink of carrots. 'There's no other choice. You know that.'

No choice. Mom's words pound in his chest. His heart, a snared rabbit. The rabbit and the snare. Both the rabbit and the hunter at once.

Laddy lurches to a stop like there's something he's forgotten. He rears back, turns and sprints for Luke. Then he stops mid-distance, sits on his hind legs, waiting for Luke to catch up.

That clueless look on his face – it could make you go crazy with hate. His one floppy ear, his tongue-out grin. He has it coming to him. A look so open and clear it shows you what you thought you'd buried deep so no one else would see.

There's no other choice. You know that. He could hike past the Leary's. Another hundred miles. A hundred miles in any direction. He could walk for days and nights. He could cross an ocean of brome and crested wheat, spear grass poking through what's left of the coarse spring snow. There's no running away. He thinks of the story Mom tells about some Aunt and Uncle. Instead of coming to Canada, they traveled north for more land. To Linejewka, Kellerowka, Liebental. Places no longer on a map. They slept on blankets beneath their cart. At night, before making up their bed, they'd open the crate to let their hens roam free. 'Why didn't they run away?' Luke always asks.

'Run away?' Mom would shake her head. 'Who? The chickens? Where were they supposed to go?'

Snares empty, Luke tramps out of the poplar thicket into their north field. Behind him there's the rustle of Laddy rooting in some slough grass. 'Laddy,' Luke calls, patting his thigh. When the dog is at his side, Luke pauses. 'Sit,' he shouts. Laddy trots forward a few more steps. 'No, Laddy. Come on.' Luke pushes down on the dog's backside. Laddy twists from Luke's hands and rolls onto his back, wriggles in the tilled dirt. Then he jerks up, sprints west. Luke squints into the low sun, looks beyond Laddy's trajectory. A jackrabbit ripping through the field. It's too far away. Laddy won't get close. Luke lifts the Mossberg to his shoulder. He's the best shot. Martin can't hit the broad side of a barn. Peter doesn't have the guts. They'd make a mess of it.

The rabbit veers right to throw off its predator. You hardly ever see a jackrabbit bounding in the field like this – only in the tricky light of dusk. Racing home to feed its young. They nest in the open, between clumps of sod; nests made from twigs and grass, knots of fur that they pluck from their own bellies. Luke watches the rabbit through the scope, its easy leap over the furrows, its glide through the purpling air. The sun falls beneath the horizon. He lowers his gun.

He's missed chores. Supper too. He circles their shelterbelt and enters the yard from the southeast. This way he can sneak up on the porch. He pauses behind the grain bins and watches the house, a blister of light against the darkening sky. Mom at the kitchen table mending socks. Peter and Martin in the bedroom, homework spread across the desk. Dad in the parlour. A newspaper. A cup of tea. Luke doesn't know what to call this aching in his bones. The moon lifts above the evergreens, a scrap of crescent cradling the faint outline of its fuller self.

There's no avoiding it. He can't hide out here forever. He wades through the unmown grass between the bins, walks the length of the machine-shed. When he turns the corner, he sees someone in the yard. Dad. Between the house and the cow barn. Back straight, staring north.

Laddy shoots ahead of Luke. Dad turns to the sound of Laddy's bark. Luke can feel Dad's gaze. Though blood pounds in his ears, he tries to not hurry his pace.

'Where were you?' Dad asks as Luke approaches. His voice low.

'Checking my snares.'

Dad stares at him like he's trying to decide. It's not a lie. Still, Luke looks to the ground between them, dusk's gauzy shadows.

'Well, then.' Dad turns for the house. 'Better get inside.'

They walk to the house like that – Luke following in the wake of Dad's scent, clean flannel, Old Spice, the dark lapping in behind him. Dad doesn't say another word but now his silence is something gentle – an arm around the shoulder, a squeeze. It's not enough, though.

Luke's bones still ache when he thinks about what he has to do. Somewhere beyond the shelterbelt a coyote sings a forsaken note, long and high. As the keen descends, others join in. Their yips and wails ripple the night air. Maybe there's no choice, but there's this: from now on he will decide for himself when it hurts.

Azul

Maria Sledmere

In search of paradise, I've been selling holidays at Tropical Nirvana: a high-street travel agent where mostly we flog package deals to families with credit scores even poorer than mine. Daily I watch them arrive and depart through revolving doors, their dull existence a potentiality that hinges on imminence: it's up to me to drag them out the loop, to offer them a sunset. It's a simple transaction: I hand them brochures; they sign the form, pay the deposit.

'A lot of money this,' they grumble, slotting away purses and pinching their lips.

Scanning my accounts, the boss constantly reminds me: *gotta keep those zeros healthy*. What's a holiday to these families? £1000 a pop for the gratitude of their children.

Not that I ever had a reason to thank my mother. She could barely peel herself off the sofa; I discovered early on that there was little chance of getting her to the shops, let alone an airport. When creditors banged on the door, when Mum retched up wine in the sink, when classmates taunted my sallow skin, I'd go to a happy place. Sanity is believing in paradise, believe me. I needed something more than the kitsch thrills of *Treasure Island* or *Moby Dick*. Needed something whose value lay in what remained when you took the 1 from 1000—a priceless destination.

Paradise: the idea of a static beauty, a place completely free from outside interference, self-contained, clear as a looped array of zeros. The core experience of your own company, communing with the sacred, self-created virtual. Work once sent us, half-jokingly, on a meditation class for team-bonding, and afterwards while we lay on the floor the woman described the soft hush of the waves, *a horizon as blue as your first love's eyes*. Everyone fell asleep but I reached another plane entirely, recalling a memory of childhood that glittered into shape from blueprints of 1s and 0s. Do you remember the default wallpapers you got with Windows XP computers? We had them at school; I remember the supernaturally green hills, the red desert with its full fake moon. My favourite was 'Azul', consisting of a miniature island, populated with a triplet of palms and surrounded by water more crystalline than any genuine turquoise. This was a paradise you couldn't just *travel to*; like something that had fallen off a map, it existed beyond a sort of portal. Still does. I used to take the little colour picker tool to select that distilled cerulean and use it for everything, writing instant messages in pastel blue and printing homework glazed with its luminous hue. People took the piss, just as my colleagues do now when they see my PC wallpaper.

'Stepping past your desk is like going back in time,' the boss has quipped, at least once.

Recently, I posted this thing about it on Yahoo answers. Some troll started telling me the photo was definitely fake, because on an island that small, there was no way three palm trees could sustain themselves without other nourishing vegetation. It was too bare, like a porn-star stripped of all their body hair; it existed purely for the camera, the screen. I refused to believe it. I down-voted his comment and a few other people chimed in with various geographical speculations. A user called 'sandybeaches' wrote: *just go there.*

*

Working late, with the customers gone home, I'm trying to teach myself code. The more time I spend working for Tropical Nirvana, the more urgent my need for building worlds. So I'm learning the crucial tools: html, Java, Visual Basic. My brain gets looped on the logic and sometimes when I talk I hear my voice reiterate the script. I'm solving problems with deductive systems, swinging the company better deals, pinning down variables. The customers love my efficiency. Machines are seductive; with binary, you pare everything back to magic causality.

Jenny comes to meet me at the office. She sort of blends into the upholstery, always wearing grey pencil skirts and shadowy green blouses, so it takes me a while to notice her. I mean, more than once I've had to blink twice to realise she's not an office plant.

'Hey,' I say, not taking my eyes off the screen. There's a load of accounts due in tomorrow but I'm practicing rendering text in motion, conjuring this image of sentences ebbing to and fro like boats in water.

'I thought we could grab dinner or something.' I know she's already glancing out the window, bored; that Mark'll be watching us closely.

'There was talk of folk going to the pub,' I say vaguely, clicking away the applications. She's fiddling with the buttons on her sleeve.

'Oh.'

'We can still go though, if you want.'

'No, I'm not bothered. I wasn't hungry, anyway.' Does she know I can see right through her? I can see through the white gauze of her blouse; her blood swimming beneath that illumined surface, its anaemic blueness catching the office light like the inside of a clam shell. The dull pulse of all those nerves: *eat, eat, eat,* flashing the off-values of her source code. She never fucking eats.

'Good,' I tell her, grabbing my jacket.

The pub is packed as always. The only place in this town that doesn't charge £4 for a pint. Gentrification gets to even the worst of places, even this side of town where the ratio of fag butts to concrete is pretty unhealthy. I queue for a good fifteen minutes around the bustling wasters you might call my comrades, then come back with a large Chardonnay for Jenny, who drinks this stuff even though it's November and just the feel of the chilled glass gives me chilblains. A couple of guys from work join us, doling out office gossip while I find myself scrolling on my phone. I wouldn't admit to a soul that I still use those old-fashioned blogging sites favoured by teenagers. It's the endlessness that I like; the implication that I could slide my finger forever and still be fed more images. Tonight, I stick to selected metadata; I prefer objects severed from context. A glistening fruit lolly, orange against purple; an iced coffee layered in white and caramel gold. They coexist nicely, achieve a lulling hum of virtual possibility. Sometimes I go home and pick them apart, honing on frayed edges, patches of pixellation that betray their compression; looking for gaps where the code can be manipulated. Always I'm wanting the origins, excavating the glossy landscape of ASCII that lies behind that lossy data, the cracked cryptogram revealing itself in isolation. I never use Facebook, bored with all its reality and scandal and demanding connection. Jenny once told me her friends think I don't exist. It's rich, coming from her. She just sits there, thin as air, and never says a word.

It's the sexting she's good at, but what do I care for a well-timed emoji, a glimpse of those tiny, sour tits and the salt-white shape of her breastbone?

'How are your stats doing, Mark?' I find myself asking, spearing him with my favourite jeering look. We have a casual office rivalry, mostly propelled by his ridiculous suspicion that I will get promoted before him.

'Sold six holidays to Jamaica today,' he brags, eyes shining from the second Guinness. 'Nailed it with my usual charm. One guy really loved my *Cool Runnings* gag.'

'Fucking racist,' Adrian says, basically spitting. He's that guy who always grimaces when he sees me, and recently I discovered it's because of his aversion to pastel-coloured ties. 'Have you ever even met a Jamaican?'

'Just banter mate,' Mark protests. 'Anyway Adrian, I don't see *you* making those destinations fly off the shelves.'

'What shelves? These aren't paperback novels. We're dealing in abstract concepts: *PARADISE, PALM TREES, POOLSIDES*. These are intangible.' Adrian stretches a dramatic pause, puckering his lips. 'There is no such thing as a palm tree. They're not even native to California. You can't feel one; every glimpse is just a glimpse of some prop from a Hollywood movie. Touch one and it crumbles; just a roughness, a ruin between your fingers. Nobody really enjoys a poolside. All those midges? Suntan grease leaking into the water? The chemicals they put in those cocktails? A Margarita is basically just an MSG slush puppy. The whole place is a biohazard. That's why it's not really a place at all, but an *Idea* we make tangible through sales tactics. It's our power to give glorious shape to the barren lands. Parts of the world made absent by their very presence as holiday destinations.'

'This is what I'm saying,' Mark replies, frustrated, 'I've *got* the tactics. I'm a born salesman.'

'Anyone else remember Teletext holidays?' I pipe up. 'They'd always be flogging these really vague competitions: *COMING SOON: TROPICAL DESTINATIONS.*'

'Mate, *Teletext holidays*?!' Mark is always astounded at my memory for these things. It's as if his whole experience of technology started with the iPhone and so everything before is impossible.

Beside me, Jenny plays with some bottle tops.

I persist. 'Like, where the fuck *are* these tropical destinations?' Whisky, cheap and cheerful, brings it out in me, the poet or whatever. Six drinks in and it's like I'm channelling text from the web, all that flotsam catching the current, the currency of my tongue. 'They could be anywhere. A paddling pool in someone's backyard, flanked by plastic gnomes and some prick playing The Piña Colada Song; a grotty wee beach in Blackpool. You never knew *what* you were getting.'

The assistant manager raises his head.

'You speak as if from experience, Adam, but Mark tells me you've never actually been abroad?' His tone is more curious than judgemental, but I'm kicking Mark under the table because the last thing I need is the boss knowing I'm a total fraud, that in reality I haven't even seen the goddamn sea—not even Blackpool.

'I-I've been around Europe,' I lie, nodding my head vigorously and tipping back another Grouse and soda. 'But I've also, crucially, been around Teletext.' God knows I had, all those summer afternoons with Mum drunk on the sofa, nothing to watch on telly, the air shimmering with static inertia. My words fall flat as Adrian crunches a peanut, snapping the silence clean in half.

'Well,' he suggests sarcastically, 'you sure do bring the world to... life.'

Jenny flashes me the look—*excruciating*—and I know it's time to go home.

I walk her back to her house where she stays on the edge of town, the suburban bit, belted round the motorway. She looks after her mother, lives with her or something. I can't remember what's wrong with the woman but Jenny's constantly using her as an excuse to get away from me. We walk quickly as I rehearse reams of code in my head, the rainy streets slushing against my tropical dreams.

'Thanks for the drink,' Jenny says wispily, her mouth creasing like paper. I kiss her the way you would stamp a postcard.

The flat is cold as usual. There's not enough money in the leccy to put the heaters on so I grab a blanket and flip open my laptop, hoping to bask in its electric breath. Webpages pass me by, skimmed by the frantic click of my fingers. I stick on my favourite ambient playlist, listening for the hypnotic purr of waves recorded on some distant, perhaps imaginary shore, picturing some guy at his decks mixing the noise to perfect pitch. It's how I orchestrate my own sales, getting that tone, that atmosphere right. I pause at a gallery of wallpapers. I roll a cigarette, pour some whisky; a text grumbles on the phone at my feet. *Azul, azul,* what actually are you? The stuff Adrian said about abstract concepts really got to me. It seems almost stupid, the sailboat, the sky and the sea... If only there were a button...

I exhale the smoke. Out of my breath, carcinogenic, my purpose clarifies its form. I start typing, the propositions coming with unusual ease. I'm arranging palimpsests of images in my brain. You follow certain functions, weave possibilities from scraps of stolen logic. AND after AND mingles with the beats and makes its THEN progression across a page of CSS, spilling down the screen like a waterfall. Nothing interesting happens. There's a precise pattern I want, the kind of program that makes the hard-drive whirr and warm just so. String data enhanced for a loop. I'm bracketing concatenations, building the nested coils of code until it runs like a spool of tape, skipping through keys until it prints onscreen the static void, a semi-colonic pause. As we move through the ELSE function, a dialogue box appears:

Hello World. It's a primitive simplicity, slipping into the loop's residue, the afterbirth of infinity.

The screen glows through the smoke. I am blinded with light, then my body touches sand. Actual, soft, baby's skin sand. The colour of pale roses, surrounded by a rippling sea. Everything pure and clean. Have I died?

(... The ocean sounds like the constant, million crackles of a crystal breaking up, its internal latticework collapsing, a symphony suspended in shimmery craquelure. John Cage burying a flock of angels. The sky the kind of blue you have to wash out with white just to get to. It's so easy to sink into objects; they yield to my touch elastically, the trunks of palms absorbing my fist as molten toffee. I drift, slowly, between one thing, another. Paradise invites me into the frame.

I have counted the trees; they are the same, a perfect three. This is solitude, this is sweetness. There are no birds. I am noticing now the lack of birds. The heatwave pulses through me; I am a machine and this is the thrum of my body. I grow more diaphanous by the hour, whatever an hour is, the trawl of the hot orange sun no indicator in the sky. Sometimes, everything suspends. The clouds stop their background drag and the water freezes. It's like glass. I am trapped in a hung universe. No cursor available, no Ctrl + Alt + Delete.

Then there is a resurgence of movement and everything is as serene as before; I hear birdsong sweet despite the absence of life, I listen to anonymous pulses in the waves. I am content to gaze upon my miniature universe, suspended without diurnal turn. Sometimes when I stare too long it comes apart. I can't explain... it's like reality's fabric reveals its strange virtual...

I am translucent, without reflection; I see the sand and the sea through my skin in sparkles. There are traces of code I recognise as ASCII, a diacritical mass scattered across surfaces of matter. Sometimes I glimpse 1s and 0s, flickering like the tiniest fish; colours fading dimly to HEX numbers. I try to plunge into the water again and again but it is just so much air, a hologram vision bright with light and texture and yet nothing, just nothing, an illusion of blue that sustains the...)

Waking is the worst part. My brain glitching up, unable to make sense of my surroundings. An ice of cold cuts into my bones. Everything hurts in the darkening.

I check my phone, which is buzzing like a terrified crab at my feet. Two missed calls from Jenny. A voicemail. *Adam, my Mum's not doing so well... I think it's time we took a break. Call me, or don't... whatever.*

I crush the plastic and hurl it at the laptop screen. An ocean shatters. The wallpaper literally splitting. I watch the liquid crystal pixels ooze, gelatinous, from the cracks. *Gotta keep those zeros healthy.* Just like that, Jenny dissolves; I can feel her digits crisping.

*

It's maybe morning, two nights later; maybe another morning, two weeks later. Sometimes, at home with my broken laptop, I revisit the wallpaper code; my brain tries to process it all, the vivid program with its impenetrable arabesques of run-on lines and faulty dialogue. I go to work, running my body like a loop; my ears still full of the sea's pink noise, only half attuned to sirens and cars, the generalised dialogue of the city. I find myself at my work PC, gazing with true affection at the screen, drunk on the bourbon I stash in my desk. On the phone, customers listen to my drawl of exhausted descriptions, the litany of a hangover: *yes, paradise palms, an azure ocean, whatever you want, we can get...* My boss admires this new docility, its extremity of machinic repetition; I suppose I've become the foil for Mark's personable enthusiasm.

'Adam,' he announces, 'I think it's time you got that promotion.' I see the wrinkles of his face undulate like dunes, feel the rose-white sand slipping once more through my quivering fingers. Doesn't he know I'm a lush?

'Time, also, that you see for yourself a slice of this paradise.' The boss hands me a ticket to a place whose name I can't pronounce.

'I know you can make it fly,' he adds with a touch of condescension, sorting the brochures on his desk. Mark casts me a wistful glance. He's known I'm a phoney all along, but neither of us give up the game.

*

Looking out from the plane window, the land and the sea crisscross in arbitrary fault-lines. We soar higher and just before the whiteness there's that endless stretch of cerulean, beaming like the light from a colossal laptop. I sense the plane juddering in upward motion, and for a moment it feels like we'll spin; that we'll loop forever between sky and sea, the parameters of dream and reality. So I grab a hostess, order a double whisky, lie back against the seat. The windows sequence the aisles with arrays of zeros, those O-gaping portals of possibility. I turn off the company phone, take a gulp of my drink and feel, for once, remarkably healthy.

Orphaned by air and space and time, I look through the glass and the blue catches me quick as a sleep.

Blue Channel

Simon Brown

Yousef's death turned out to be the shot in the arm our relationship needed. Being married for forty years doesn't necessarily mean that the two of you will find yourselves in a rut, but it does make it more likely. So when he received his diagnosis and was given only a month or two to live, it was as if we were starting again from scratch.

We started talking again, covering every topic imaginable, under the guise of giving the implant as much material as possible. We said all the things we'd ever wanted to say but thought too insignificant. We joked and laughed, only to have his illness muscle its way in and smother the atmosphere. There was a gap of silence after every laugh where I could tell that he too was wondering if that would be the last one we'd share.

They dug out the implant while his body was still warm. After the funeral – attended by me, and the person operating the furnace – I sat at home, staring at the shiny metal box that contained Yousef. The grief numbed me to the point that it was meditative. I lost hours. When the doorbell rang and I got up every one of my bones clicked.

A courier. I pressed my thumb against its touchscreen and it dropped the box into my arms and floated away over the estate.

It took me ages to open the box, my hands were shaking so badly. The urn was a sunset orange with two giant handles on either side. I prodded it. Nothing. I tilted it – carefully – to see if the bottom had an on switch, but all I found was the name of the company and the model number.

It wasn't until I poured the ashes in that something happened. Dots appeared on the urn's surface and floated slowly towards the bottom, where, layer-by-layer, a shape took form.

It was him. It was my Yousef from the shoulders up, only he had been stylised to look like the figures that adorned pottery from thousands of years ago. He blinked, then grinned. His smile was unmistakeable.

'How long was I gone?'

I couldn't answer. I smeared the tears across my cheeks and stared at him in disbelief.

His eyes opened wide. 'I don't look that bad do I?'

I coughed up some laughter. 'I've missed you.'

The playful look vanished from his face. 'I missed you too. But I'm here again. Just like always. Look,' he said, shrinking so that the whole of his body was visible, 'when was the last time you saw me do this?' He did some starjumps, followed by a few laps of the urn. I suddenly became very aware of how stiff my limbs felt.

Yousef stopped running and leaned forward on his thighs, panting. 'This doesn't make sense,' he said between breaths. 'Why am I tired?'

I laughed. 'Maybe because the real you never ran a day in your life.'

Silence swamped us. He looked sad. I pinched the skin of my palm. 'I didn't mean...' I began, but I didn't know what it was I didn't mean. He *wasn't* real; he was a computer's approximation of him. My Yousef wasn't some big, expansive character but it couldn't have sussed the entirety of him in only a few short weeks.

Little spirally rainclouds appeared on the urn and spat diagonal lines. 'I am me,' he said. 'I'm right here. I thought you'd be pleased.'

I spent the rest of the evening in the kitchen. It was like I was ten again and my house was full of aunts, uncles and cousins from far-flung places, jabbering amongst themselves in a language I was only vaguely familiar with. I could never sleep with those strangers in my house and, as I stood there listening to Yousuf humming to himself, I knew my position hadn't softened in the last seventy or so years.

It was as I was contemplating sneaking out of the kitchen window that Yousuf began to sing. His voice was unmistakeable; it was as it had been towards the end of his life, full of cracks and creases that had an authenticity even the most technically accomplished singer couldn't fake.

I crept through to the living room and stood leaning against the jamb. He was sitting on what I imagined was supposed to be a cliffedge, singing to a glum looking moon.

'Laying it on a bit thick, don't you think?'

'Try having someone tell you that you're not real and see how happy you feel.'

I left the jamb and shuffled towards the urn. 'I'm sorry,' I said, 'but put yourself in my place for a second. Yousef died only a few days ago. I haven't even begun to think about how I'll never get to hold him again, or warm my feet up against him on cold winter nights. And now there's you, this cartoon version of him. Sure, you sound and look like him, but you aren't actually him.'

Yousef left the cliffedge and walked towards me until all I could see was his face. 'The eleventh of October. There was a big group of us, all drinking, and I couldn't keep my eyes off you. Everything you did – the way you laughed, the way you took a drink, the way you smoothed your skirt as you stood up to go to the bar – it all seemed so elegant.'

The hairs on my arms sprung up. I said nothing.

'I kept wanting to talk to you but you were over on the other side and I couldn't think of a reason to go over there that wouldn't look so bloody obvious. So I drank. And drank.'

I stared down at my hands and fiddled with my ring.

'And that was when I noticed the fire alarm.'

I laughed and looked up at him again. 'Okay, I get it. You remember.'

'Exactly. So that means I'm me, yeah?'

It was hard to argue with him. I bought him a papoose and took him on walks with me. As we walked – or rather shuffled – he'd recall things that we'd done over the years to drive home the point that he was who he said he was. In between these recollections he'd scatter some bizarre information about the trees or buildings we passed, their names and histories. It was the kind of thing he'd never have known while he was alive, but since he was now able to access a wealth of information I suppose he felt the need to show off.

'How about those flowers, there,' he said as we walked past a garden filled with crimson snapdragons, 'do you like them?'

I stopped and watched the bees bounce from petal to petal. 'They're very pretty.'

'I know a website we can get them cheaply. Maybe I should buy us some.'

'Oh. Um. No. It's okay. Thanks though.'

'Go on. They'd be perfect in the living room.'

He spoke with such enthusiasm that it was difficult to say no a second time, so I didn't.

I hobbled over to the mantelpiece and stuck the vase in between a couple of photographs. The petals were so delicate I could've been touching his hand.

'You see?' he said, 'they add a wonderful sparkle to the room. Only...'

I looked up from the picture of the two of us in front of Blackpool Tower. 'Only what?'

'Only they don't really go with the curtains, do they?'

He was right. I'd always hated those noxious beige curtains but whenever I brought up the idea of replacing them my Yousef would just grunt something non-committal and, when pressed, mutter about the state of our finances. So, naturally, it delighted me to find he'd come round to my way of thinking.

'Something blue would work, maybe,' I said, 'what do you think?'

'I think you should've been an interior designer. Want me to order some for us?'

I watched the swampy mess billowing in the breeze. 'Yes,' I said, a thrill zapping through me, 'do it.'

This urn version of Yousef was far more involved in the drudgery of household maintenance than his flesh counterpart had ever been. He ordered new cleaning products, dishcloths and food before I'd even realised we'd run out and, upon seeing me struggling with a manual peeler, went and ordered an electric one. Hardly a bouquet of roses, I know, but it was still a marked improvement on his old self.

I became so accustomed to the daily visits from the courier that the ring of the doorbell no longer carried with it a jolt of excitement. I'd long given up imagining on my way to the door that it was some long lost cousin or a niece or nephew that wanted to welcome us into their lives.

It was after one of these visits from a courier that I found myself in possession of a preposterously huge television. I managed to carry it through under one arm – they'd certainly advanced since I'd last had one – and set it down right in front of Yousef.

'Know anything about this?'

'Ah, it arrived. Fantastic. I thought over there might be a good spot.'

'You bought this?'

'Of course I did. Go on, get it unpacked and see how it looks over there.'

'You can't just buy things without asking me.'

Yousef scoffed. 'Wouldn't be much of a surprise then, would it?'

'But we can't afford it.'

'Not all in one lump sum, no. But they had a very generous credit offer.'

'Send it back.'

'What? You haven't even tried it yet. You should see some of the prog-'

'I'm serious. Send it back.'

'Fine.'

The urn went blank.

I spent the rest of the evening pottering about in an eerie silence. Every now and then I'd make some comment, some banal observation, only to be met with silence. I felt his absence more keenly then. I tried to pretend he was in the other room, or that he'd just nipped out, but my brain wouldn't believe it even for a second. I buried my face in the sheets on his side of the bed – I couldn't bring myself to wash them yet – but his smell was gone. I had nothing. Only this stupidly large television.

I tried to read but found my eyes tripping over the same sentence again and again, so, in frustration, I approached the slim cardboard box that I'd propped up against the wall. It came out easy enough and had set itself up within a few seconds of me turning it on.

'Glad you came to your senses,' said Yousef. Even though it had only been a few hours the sound of his voice was an immense relief to me. The little taste of loneliness I'd had was enough to make me grateful he was speaking to me again.

He picked a channel. The screen filled with an arresting shade of lapis, accompanied by a low, constant tone. I'd never really been into the abstract programming that passed for entertainment now, but there was something peculiar about this particular shade of blue and this tone that drew me in. It seemed to burn away the residual unpleasantness of the last few hours and replaced it with an understated sort of calm. I could see now why traditional drama had fallen by the wayside.

I turned to Yousef. Pride prevented me from actually saying the word 'sorry' but I think he understood it from the smile I gave him.

After that I found it much more difficult to argue with him whenever he bought something. The possibility of the silent treatment hung over every new purchase, whether it was the tacky little robot bird that kept crashing into things or a state of the art fridge freezer.

I was sitting on the shiny new leather couch, ignoring the idiot bird's digital chirping coming from the locked cupboard, when I noticed the urn looked a little strange. A dark smear covered most of its surface and at the end of it was Yousef's face, juddering backwards and forwards in tiny movements.

'Yousef?'

His eyes found mine and his expression changed but the juddering continued. He tried to say something but whatever it was got caught on the first syllable, making a whirring sort of sound. I cried out and scooped him up in my arms. Strange objects appeared and disappeared in the space around the smear. Everything went blank. I shook it. Hit it. Begged it. Nothing.

He was gone.

I had watched him die a second time.

I needed to be calm. Numb. I switched on the screen. Scrolled through dross, adverts.

'...that even those who aren't as rich as they'd like should have access to digital life extension.' I stopped scrolling. A woman sat at a sunny picnic table next to an urn that contained a man who was looking at her with a deep sort of love in his eyes. Bees, butterflies and blossom danced all around them. Her eyes met his for a second, then looked back at the camera. 'That's why we've launched our ad-based eTruscan range. So even if...'

An email popped up on the bottom right of the screen. 'OVERDUE'. Big red letters.

I switched to the blue channel.

Flying Saucers

Eleanor Capaldi

The sherbet is sharper on my tongue than I remember, but then the outside casing goes to mush and soothes the sting.

Flying Saucers, they used to be a fixture in my 10p mix, but that was more than ten years ago now. These perfect pockets of sweetness look sturdy enough, but they've dissolved in only a few soft sucks. The pink is probably the beetroot dyed one. Beetroot is poisonous if you eat too much of it, goes for your kidneys. They told me that at the Poison Garden in Alnwick, where I went as an adult.

They all taste disappointingly the same even in their different colours; yellow, white, pink, green; sharp sting, slow mush.

As a kid, my imagination didn't know how to curtail itself – the discarded pine tree wasn't a pine tree, it was a dinosaur skeleton in the back garden. And there was a lost civilisation in the dirt, evidenced by blue pottery shards. It was entirely believable that a daffodil could grow from an acorn. There was a story in everything. Sweets didn't need to be more than a treat, pure fun, there was nothing to be comforted from, except maybe skint knees, and bee stings.

These discs, every one a Saturn, with their protruding circumferences, were a trip to space, and an invite to pilot a rocket ship. That's how it started, with a dream of stars, wishing on them, as we all do, and then flying up to see them too.

But it's over 10 years later, and 10p mixes are now 20 pence for the same amount. There are daydreams and night dreams and nightmares, flights of fancy, and what ifs, but they tend to congregate around fears, and emanate from worries. There are no dinosaurs out the back, only branches and bone like bark, scattered.

The Bastard Octopus

Heather Parry (after Roland Barthes)

The limbs of the costumed cephalopod wrap around his opponent and tighten, rendering the man inert. The crowd give heat; as one, they jeer and boo, a disguised adoration. They live for this. They spit their pantomime displeasure onto the skin of others. They breathe in the foetid stench of the fighters, see the tears of sweat drip from one man to the other. They suckle at soda teats and scream themselves hoarse at the injustice they expect and demand. In the ring, the trapped man is scooped, three arms between his legs and three around his neck, lifted like he is weightless, held for a moment then slammed down onto the canvas. The impact of the body disperses droplets of blood from a puddle in the wet ring. The blood of other wrestlers, of fights before theirs. The crowd react with manic outrage. It is sweeter than usual.

The stunned body rises. Steadies itself. The Bastard Octopus resists, holding back from the easy attack. This is his role, but he does not want it. Cheers. Goading. Parts of him respond to the coaxing. His dexterous arms swim as if casting a spell. They linger in the air. They wait. And then; they grab. They wrap. The other fighter's hands respond, the two lock up, but six arms overpower two. The crowd surges forward to look for mechanics, electronics, engineering. They marvel at the smooth movement of the antagonist, the way his arms seem part of him. The Bastard Octopus fills himself up, draws all power into his chest, pauses, drives his opponent into the turnbuckle. The thrown man sags and slips to the canvas. There is no movement. The crowd ignites. The fight is over quickly, too quickly for the money they have paid, but they don't mind. They come for the righteous indignation. They leave satisfied.

The Bastard Octopus retires to his dressing room. The other fighters bathe in the women and booze that come to them. They gather sweaty and imbibe intoxicants, their manufactured gripes left in the ring. The Bastard Octopus does not join them. He rushes to his solitude. Behind the closed door, he slips his two legs and six arms out of his outfit, an outfit that has been cleverly created to give four of his upper limbs the illusion of fakeness. He slides into the shower, employing four bars of soap and all his appendages to the mammoth task of freshening his armpits, then towels off with impressive speed. He stands at the mirror, looking for injuries. None.

He takes his lowest arm and presses bicep to torso. He bends it at the elbow, wrapping it around his stomach. He does the same with his next arm, which sits atop the first. He does the same with all of his lower four, forming a protective shell around his upper body, then he takes an elastic bandage and wraps. The arm shell tightens. The bandage constricts. He adds an inch or so of girth, but not more. Swaddled in himself, only two arms free, he struggles into a shirt and then a hoodie, despite the fact that he will sweat through both. He turns the light in the hallway off before he strides down it, head bowed, trying not to catch the attention in the fighters at the bar as he makes for his vehicle. Someone shouts something, but he's learned not to hear.

The Bastard Octopus spends nights at his local gym. In the absence of other customers, he whiles away the hours until sunrise training. He squats, letting his favoured arms hold the bar and willing the rest to stay by his side. But the arms still reach up, still try to ease the burden of the weight. They are part of him, but he cannot control them. He attempts to train not his upper arms, not his legs, not his glutes, but the arms that move despite him. He lifts and carries and pushes but it is the unwanted appendages that he concentrates on, willing them to stay down, to lose function, to flop around gracelessly. But they do not. They press their palms to the floor and lift his body. They grab the tyre, the kettlebell, the pull up bar. They act, and he cannot stop them. Exhausted, as the day breaks, he heads home—to sleep, to hide, to wait for the night.

As his next match nears, he calls a number that has been given to him online, in forums, where he uses a fake female name and complains of ageing. The voice at the end of the line expresses concern about the amounts requested, triples the agreed-upon fee and tells him where to pick up a package. In a darkened garage, under the cover of night, The Bastard Octopus stuffs the contraband into his bandages and races back to his car.

He cannot afford to waste any of the material on testing. He stands in front of his mirror as at the end of the corridor, the crowd screech and boo at the wrestlers already engaged in the ring. He stands naked, costume-free, and cracks the first syringe out of its housing. He takes the cold point and traces it along the bicep of his lowest arm. He pauses a moment then slams the needle into the muscle. A straight pain. He expends it, empties the barrel. Feels a breeze rush into the tiny hole left by the needle. He tosses the used syringe into an old tool box he's brought for the purpose, and starts the process over again, this time with the forearm. He waits. Heat envelops the arm, spreading out from the shoulder to the tips of his nails. The muscles shake, fight against the toxin. Perspiration covers his skin. The arm becomes leaden, drops. Overtaken by a flaccid paralysis. Beaming, The Bastard Octopus punches the arm with a spare fist. It hangs, limp, useless. He could weep. He takes the remaining syringes and goes through it all again; eight syringes, in total, for four arms. Bundling the lifeless appendages clumsily into the arms of his costume, he turns his body from side to side like a child. Four of his arms flop, slap, knock things over. Outside the door, his name is called. Ecstatic, he runs to the ring, heavy and cumbersome, lolling like a weighted ship. He drags his mass into the humid ring and surrenders.

The Bastard Octopus never reads the script, for his body never follows the script.

When the fighter comes for him, he is loose and unprepared. He is punched. He is lifted, arms encircling his torso, his eyes closed. His upper back slams to the ground as he is suplexed first once, then twice, then a third time. The pain of it is sweet, narcotic; he looks to his arms, prostrate on the canvas, twitching in agony. The crowd murmurs, unsure. This is unwritten, to their minds. The heel has turned victim. His opponent grabs his hand, lifts one of his active arms, and wraps his thick legs around it. He laces his fingers around the Bastard Octopus's wrist, his crotch against the covered skin, lets himself fall back onto the canvas, and wrenches the arm from its socket. For a moment, The Bastard Octopus feels his arm removed from his body, tendons ripped, chest muscle separated from ligament. His heart seizes; the loss of it stuns him. He feels impotent. Six down to one. What has he done? The crowd is quiet, near-silent. He is hauled to his feet, steadied, set up for another attack. He clutches his one strong arm to the one numb and detached; he feels the rest of them stir, want to help, want to reach up and assist. The torn arm twitches. He breathes. It is still stitched to his body. He pushes all his effort into movement; it shifts. It remains. It tingles, but so do the others. He is still whole. He grimaces, a true reaction, but not for the reasons the audience assume. The other fighter is gleeful, intending to hurt. He steps back, giving distance, creating a show. He plays to the audience, receives little response, and grows angrier. The Bastard Octopus closes his eyes as the man runs at him, readying his bent body for a running drop kick aimed right at the head.

The crowd detonates. Screeching cheers that burn the ears. He opens his eyes; the other fighter has been flung past him, over the ropes, over the guard rail, into the braying crowd. Red-faced and raging, the man climbs back into the ring, mounts the turnbuckle, prepares himself for a vengeful pounce. He jumps. Flies. The Bastard Octopus watches as his four heavy arms, rendered obsolete just moments ago, raise themselves up and catch the man, wrapping him, chest to chest, lifting him and slamming him onto the canvas with an aggression that pains them both. From there, he cannot watch. Inside him, a rock falls down an endless well. His eyes are open but he does not see the rest. He does not need to. It has all been written, and the crowd are delighted.

Five wins in a row. Seven. Twelve. The crowds grow and grow but the promoters aren't happy. They tell him to hang back, to stand off, to let the others get a few moves in, a few wins. But he cannot. With incredible will he can hold off his own body for a short while, but eventually it takes over. Mere minutes of restraint, just a little fair contest, then he reaches out, embraces his opponent, crushes the body to his chest, overwhelms him. The crowds keep coming, and so he keeps being booked, but the other fighters pour drinks on him as he leaves the ring, leave shit in his gear bag, hammer nails into his tyres. They, too, think that the arms are mere costuming; a gimmick, a trick of the senses. They think him a cheat, and a freak one at that.

At the mirror, the Bastard Octopus flexes, spreads out like a peacock. His hated arms are growing, filling out, taking up more space. The effort of throwing and crushing huge bodies stimulate them. More bandage is needed to wrap them against him, and the resulting bulk is harder to hide. In the day, he cannot sleep, for no matter where he turns, there's a limb beneath him. On his few necessary trips into the society of others, he looks gross, a lumpen creature, knocking pensioners and children out of the way though he doesn't even see them.

Twenty wins in a row and the fight time down to seconds. They have to book his fights at the end of others, to avoid real displeasure from the spluttering, screeching crowd who now pay double. He is a destroyer, and the other fighters come away with broken bones and loose teeth. They place increasing demands on the promoters for his removal, but the promoters see the money streaming in and act only to placate. After each match, the uninjured fighters wait for him in the car park. Set at him with iron bars and baseball bats—but always beneath the neck, always at the torso, keeping his resulting injuries from being so easily seen. One beating is so brutal that when he unbinds his torso and his hidden arms fall free, one lies limp and desolate and remains that way for days. The Bastard Octopus, buoyed, feels a hope grow within him.

He loads the bar with another weight. There are only two left on the floor. Sitting beneath the apparatus, he takes deep breaths. He has pre-emptively consumed codeine, whisky, marijuana, but he knows it will still hurt. The fuzziness will be sliced through like soft cheese, but there is nothing left to do. He meditates as much as he can, lays his two lowest arms on the floor, where he has marked lines with chalk. His arms are at a strange angle and cannot lie flat, but he supposes this will help the results. With his uppermost hands, he rolls the bar along the platform he has created. He teases it along with his fingers, towards the edge, and in a moment it drops. The white filter of trauma engulfs him; his ears buzzing, his tongue fat and dry, his mouth screaming miles from his ears. When he stops writhing, he looks to the bar, which has rolled off his arms, over to the edge of the room and cracked the bottom of the mirror. His two arms are snapped, covered in blood, skewered by smashed bone. Euphoria overcomes him. Energized by frantic shock, he takes himself to his car, drives home, collapses into bed. When he wakes, his breaks are healed, the agony remaining, but his ruined arms still move, still act, still dance in time with the rest of them. In a matter of days they function fully. The promoter calls, booking the biggest fight of his life. He prepares with a listless horror. It has been written.

The Bastard Octopus stands, his hand raised by the referee, the sell-out crowd hawking and screeching, snarling and snapping, pushing the heads of others out of their view. Beside him, the rising star of the wrestling world, the new face of the company. The Bastard Octopus is under strict instruction to look up at the lights, to lay down and take his loss with little damage to his opponent. He hears a whispered reminder but brushes it away. He is a man committed. There is no going back.

The all-star swings at him with a lariat, his arm solid, unyielding. The Bastard Octopus flips backwards, crashes to canvas, heavy. The tension within him is gone. He is in no hurry. His arms stay prone, ready. A physical patience. He is thrown and pummelled, canvas at his back, at his front, against his teeth. Serenity overtakes him. A quiet in his mind. This is no work; no dance of pretended violence. The reality of the hurt is meditative. The time comes. A brief respite from his opponent. He rises up. He lifts all six of his arms, each one engaged, each one accepted, and envelops the man running towards him. Stopped, the man yelps. Six biceps strain to keep him in place, distended veins mapping his skin, sweat pouring. Six hands fasten themselves around the limbs, around the torso, around the neck. Six arms lift the body, almost throw him upwards, pause, then in one explosive motion, smash him merielessly into the ground. The canvas gives, bounces back, sends the ruined spine briefly upwards again. Then it settles, the carcass at the wrestler's feet, and the audience, words caught in their throats, scream a dense silence. The only sound: a withered groaning from the broken man, an involuntary noise from collapsed lungs, a rattle. Six fists dig nails into palms; six trails of blood drip slowly. The Bastard Octopus takes in the derision, the hatred, the spite. Real. Alone amongst the frozen tableau, he lifts the ropes and leaves the ring. No one comes to stop him.

He showers. Towels down. Does not wrap his arms, nor cover himself with clothes, but leaves his dressing room bare-chested with his chin held high. Backstage there is no one, no drinkers at the bar.

He knows it is coming. He steps out into the night and fixes his eyes on the metal. He ducks, unconsciously, so the iron bar hits his forehead, not his nose as intended. After that, a soft nothing.

He wakes in his bed. He is glad that he is not in hospital, with their gross testing and inevitable labels. Around his bed there is medical equipment. Bunches of flowers, boxes of chocolates, cards saying Get Well Soon. The promoters have paid for this; he knows, then, that it was another fighter that did the damage. This is hush-hush care. That he is still so valuable to them means he has not been shopped to a hospital, to the press, to a medical researcher. But still, he is alone, cared for by electronics. He is comforted by this. By his bed there is a printed sheet:

Please do not attempt to move. You have suffered a spinal injury. You are strapped to a brace. Someone will check on you in the morning and will help you if you are awake.

Outside, the sun is almost hidden. The Bastard Octopus closes his eyes, and for the first time in his adult life, sleeps in the darkness.

The nurse comes three times a day. She explains to him that along with his fractures and breaks, he has damaged his spinal cord, making his prognosis difficult. One day, with wriggling toes, he is allowed free of his brace and sits up, slightly unsteady but confident. He shakes his legs, turns his head, coughs. The nurse is stunned. He goes to push himself up off the bed, but something is wrong. His hands—he does not know where they are. The sense of feeling their space in the world, their location, their actions—it is missing. He looks down and three of his hands are on the bed, three at his side. He attempts to move them; two twitch, make fists. He tries again. The fingers of one hand straighten and pulse, the others remain still. He cannot sense them from the inside, does not know what they are doing. A tide of immense calm comes over him. He is absolved.

Months later. The limbs of the costumed cephalopod flail and grab, some useless at his side, some at his head, some around his opponent, dropping away, letting go, grabbing again. Through rehab, he has learned some control of his upper arms; when he watches them, he can make them act. The rest, however, act sporadically, independently, without order. He lurches towards his opponent, grabs him, lifts the body a few feet off the ground, hurls it down, sees it spring back up again. The days of crushing spines are over. He is warm with the realization.

His opponent runs the ropes and sets up for a clothesline. The Bastard Octopus hides his grin as he watches the man approach. The crowd, half-empty, jeers lethargically. He has turned face, is an innocent, and they no longer crave him, nor wish for his destruction, because they do not believe in his change.

After his defeat, The Bastard Octopus stands at the mirror, uncostumed, looking for injuries. Gashes bleed and bruises bloom. One hand is curled into a broken fist; he tries to unwrap the fingers with another hand, but cannot. He closes his eyes and feels the weightless nothingness of the arms at the side of his body. His reality. No more façade. He sways on his feet and feels whole.

The Gutter Interview: Louise Welsh

Louise Welsh is the author of eight novels including *The Cutting Room*, *The Girl on the Stairs*, and *Death is a Welcome Guest*, the final volume of *Plague Times Trilogy*. She has received numerous awards and international fellowships, including an honorary fellowship from the University of Iowa's International Writing Program. She is the editor of several anthologies, as well as a playwright and librettist. Louise is Professor of Creative Writing at the University of Glasgow and lives in the city's West End with her partner Zoë Strachan.

*

R A Davis: To begin at the beginning, last year marked fifteen years since you first published *The Cutting Room*.

Louise Welsh: It's a long time.

RD: Re-reading the novel recently, it conjures up an era of Glasgow at a certain time; the antique dealers, the backstreet businesses, an era that perhaps looks back to the twentieth century rather than forward to the twenty-first. Do you feel that it captured a moment in the world in general, or in Glasgow specifically?

LW: It's funny, I've not read that book since I handed it in, probably sixteen years ago. So, when I think about

it I think about a memory of writing the book, a memory of images that I had when I was writing it. I of course had been a second-hand book-dealer – I was still a second-hand book-dealer when I started writing it – so that world of antiques was very present and real to me. In a sense we were responding to things which are still reverberating now, I think antiques, pictures, all of that kind of thing, they've always been popular, people always wanted them, but there was a point when people – a particular demographic, folk who'd done rather well from their houses and were buying bigger houses – were furnishing these homes, people who we might not have expected to be able to own large properties. They were delighted with the whole thing, you know, and we're still feeling the reverberations of that. I guess what I'm talking about is that idea of house sales, selling, reinvesting, buying, going up the ladder, which anyone who says now, to any of us, 'oh I never saw the housing crisis coming', they're either a liar or they're very foolish, because of course people were speaking out all over the place against council house sales, and we're now harvesting that particular sowing.

I didn't write it with that thought in mind but we knew that there was a whole growth in antiques and so forth, and the Square Yard at the Barras. Which is not to say that the people who were selling there were making huge amounts of money, because they weren't. That trade, for the most part, it was hand to mouth, with the odd moment of 'wahey!' [laughs], you know, of joyousness, and I think maybe *The*

Cutting Room captures that; living hand to mouth, living by your knowledge. But at the same time people look at antique dealers and they go 'oh, you know, Jack the lad, ripping people off.' Jack the lads exist, but for the most part if people wanted to be thieves they'd do it in a more profitable way.

I suppose another aspect of the book is sexuality. The period in which it is set is very different from now. I would never have imagined equal marriage – to be honest, it wasn't really very high on my list [laughs], but equality's always high up on the list so equal marriage then becomes high on the list. At points of despair, when you think nothing political ever changes, I remember that change. The difference between the world that Rilke inhabits, and the world we inhabit now. It was the moment when Soutar – Lord Soutar as he is now, who runs all the buses – you can't travel around Scotland on public transport without giving that man money – was bankrolling the vote to keep Clause 28, so I think a lot of my anger against that went into this book. Crime fiction is often socially aware, it is reflects society. I guess the other big change between the world of *The Cutting Room* and now is that in the novel everybody's smoking indoors [laughs].

RD: In *The Cutting Room*, there are a few references to the internet, very brief ones, and to mobile phones – I think Rilke has a mobile phone. But that world hasn't yet invaded. And particularly the kind of pornography referenced in the book is what we might think of as a 'vintage' idea of physical photographs. Could a story like that take place in the present, or is it now done away with because of the internet?

LW: Yeah – well I guess there must be a lot of nostalgic porn mustn't there? But, this was a point in Scotland, when people were just becoming conscious of human trafficking. I remember – I can still see the man's face actually, quite viscerally – watching television and a Police Inspector talking about women being trafficked from the Eastern Europe. He said something like, 'this could be happening in a house near you...' and just feeling this mixture of anger and sadness and shock, and then walking about and looking at the tenements around me. This idea of nefarious things going on behind closed doors has always been a central part of Scottish literature. But the realisation of the commercial trafficking people from another country for sexual purposes, and then the realisation that, not only is this happening, but that there's a lively market for it in my on neighbourhood was shocking. As a writer, a younger writer at that point – I was also thinking 'how do I write about these things without reproducing them?' Crime fiction – genre fiction, whatever we want to call it – is often socially aware, and if it's socially aware, it will date in its particulars, although the themes perhaps will still continue.

RD: On the subject of Rilke, at that point in Scottish Lit, it felt like readers hadn't experienced a fully-realised LGBT protagonist. Do you feel like Rilke's less alone now, that there are more characters, more voices, being brought to the page?

LW: He'll always be alone! He's a lonely guy walking around. [laughs] Ehm yeah, I hope so. I'm sure there must have been LGBT Scottish characters as well, because you know you're always wary of saying 'this is the first one'. Certainly today there are lots of other LGBTQ+ writers, and writers who don't identify as LGBTQ+ writing queer characters, which is all to the good I think.

RD: I just couldn't think of any that struck me personally as much as the character of Rilke does.

LW: Rilke actually has sex. There's nothing coy about Rilke. He's not tortured by his sexuality – that was really important for me. He is somebody who doesn't believe being queer is wrong, he doesn't have guilt about that. He always has safe sex – nobody ever notices that, I made sure he always has safe sex! [laughs] And it's always consensual, even though he might be out in the park, and all the rest – well, you know, great! Al fresco – but he's not tortured.

RD: It's that combination of sexuality being incidental but also central, believable. As he was your first protagonist in a novel, do you still think of him, do you think he's still wandering around the West End sometimes, getting on for 65?

LW: Oooh, well, I think about going back to him, because as you say things have changed so very much, in terms of sexuality, but also the internet and antique dealing, you know, how does that work – it's a very different trade, the antiques trade. So I do think about going back. I don't know if I'd age him in real-time, because as a novelist

you have that choice don't you. Yeah I think it would be interesting wouldn't it, because although you have Tinder and Grindr and all those things in terms of sexuality, people themselves don't change. Rilke could go on Grindr, but would he want to do that rather than go into the park? There's a whole other aspect to his nocturnal ramblings that he might himself feel nostalgic for. So, I don't know, there's a lot to think about there.

RD: You studied the masters in Creative Writing at the Universities of Glasgow and Strathclyde. Was that where you completed *The Cutting Room*?

LW: I didn't really start *The Cutting Room* until towards the end of my second year. So, I submitted part of it for my portfolio, but I think maybe I had ten to fifteen thousand words. I didn't have a huge amount. When I was there I was working mainly on short fiction, none of which really saw the light of day. But I think it was part of getting my craft together. Finding the voice of Rilke was really important. But also having that push from Zoë Wicomb, my mentor, who said 'Louise I don't think these short stories are working. I think you should work on something longer. I think you should start a novel.' And I said, 'oh Zoë, I don't know about that.' And she said 'for God's sake, go home and start a novel, and bring me the beginning of it next week.' That kind of direction might not work for everyone. But it was what I needed.

RD: And in terms of the timescale of your career, ten years later you were writer in residence at the University of

Glasgow and the Art School, and five year's after that you are the Professor of Creative Writing at Glasgow.

LW: Yes, my course fees were a good investment, weren't they!

RD: One could say that your career in particular shows the effectiveness of the university creative writing model. And you've seen the process from both sides, as a student and a teacher, as it's changed over time. What have your impressions of that been?

LW: I think it's got more rigorous. I think I got a lot of what I needed, but I think that we ask more of our students now. But that's natural as a course develops. I don't want to say gets better, as I had such a wonderful experience. But the programme becomes more developed. I certainly couldn't have had a better mentor than I had then. Today we have a huge visiting speaker programme which I am very enthusiastic about. Another key pleasure is trying to enable opportunities for other writers, whether they be current students, former students or just writers that have come into your orbit. Maybe this is a thing we benefit from in Scotland, in being a small country –whilst I hope being outward looking, and looking across the seas – we can help each other and we can pull each other up.

One of the things that I love about our programme is that we choose the writers we take on. We're not told by somebody else, these are the writers you should work with. I also love that there are lots of outside projects involved. I think it's a proper community, and it's a community where ideas are exchanged. So, Will Self saying that it's just some kind of industry which generates writers who can't make enough money. I guess it comes back to the antique business as well, you do it because you find it interesting and you believe in it.

RD: Significant parts of your novels are Glasgow-based. The final *Plague Times* novel, *No Dominion* takes us into a post-apocolyptic Glasgow, where the climax of the trilogy takes place. Living and working here, I'm wondering how the environment has changed as a writing prompt, as a muse, over the course of your career?

LW: Shops and cafes and things that have come and gone, Glasgow's certainly become more multicultural in that period, which I think we would agree is a good thing. Districts change, Partick has changed in the last six months to a year, suddenly we've got all this plastic neon, and the Chinese restaurants and things. Finnieston – who saw that coming! Gentrification. And then there are things that haven't changed at all, there are places that stay exactly the same. Some change is great, others ill-starred. You go back and look at where Mrs Jaconelli was and there's nothing really there, you know, where her beautiful flat was – what did they build instead?

RD: How have those changes influenced your writing? Particularly with *No Dominion*, and literally destroying the city –

LW: That was such a pleasure! [laughs] Why would it be a pleasure to destroy a place I really love? But it was somehow thrilling to walk around and imagine it – because it's a fantasy, because it's not going to happen, because we're fortunately in not living somewhere where the drones are coming for us. To think about how Glasgow would look, were it to be left without attention for a period of seven years. It's not actively being destroyed, it's just not had any attention and that means that fires start and nature intrudes. But I was also thinking back to the colonial past of the city– I don't want to give away too much – there are statues that are toppled, shall we say, and nods to the colonial past of Scotland within that decrepitude. Possibly nobody notices them apart from me, but that's alright. That was a joy, you know, to just go around pushing over these monuments. [laughs]

RD: Your other novels have gone to other cities, notably London, Berlin – London is your birthplace –you've travelled widely, you've spent time in other parts of the world, but apart from Glasgow, where do you feel most at home?

LW: Well I was born in London but I only spent the first year of my life there. My Dad was in the RAF and we travelled a lot when I was a child. I was brought up mainly in Edinburgh, so I guess I would say I feel most at home in Scotland. I lived in Germany for about 18 months and go back there from time to time. I speak the language very badly. There's the United States too – I've lived there for three month periods – though I haven't been there since Donald Trump came into power. Maybe feeling at home's not a priority, but it's good to have somewhere where you can call home. For me that's Scotland, and I'm lucky to travel around Scotland quite a lot. I enjoy knowing my way around different Scottish towns and cities – turn left here and right there and you'll find a café – or a particular pub. That doesn't sound very ambitious, does it? [laughs]

RD: Do you imagine you'll ever set a novel outside of Europe?

LW: Yeah, I think I could imagine doing that – though I don't have any plans to. I could imagine setting something in the United States – I've spent a bit of time in those small college towns, and I find them fascinating. Maybe they have some of that sensibility that Scottish literature is so drawn towards, these very respectable places, where you know that there's hazing, you know that there's people getting smashed, drinking a lot, a high drug intake etc. That contrast between surface, and what's beneath the surface, is always interesting isn't it? But maybe that's a cliché – could anyone do it better than David Lynch?

Zoë Strachan and I spent three months in New Zealand on a Scottish Writers' residency hosted by University of Otago, last year. That is a really interesting place as well. Beautiful landscape and really lovely people. Then I'd look at the court reports in the paper and the things that were happening… The court reports were just… if these crimes of violence happened in our country they'd be front page news, but they weren't front page news because there's so much of it.

RD: When you were in that part of the world I understand you visited places associated with Robert Louis Stevenson, because he's one of your heroes, and

I wondered what you've taken from that experience?

LW: Zoë and I went to Samoa. It is possibly the most beautiful place I have been to outside of Scotland, and the people were so welcoming and so charming and so lovely, and everything was just good. The people resisted colonisation, except by various churches [laughs], big churches everywhere. I liked the whole system though. I liked the way that families lived together, although – you know, would I like to live with my extended family? I really like them, but no! [laughs]. That's my Dad's dream: that we would all just live in a big house together.

RD: Thinking about travel and writers going to other places, what do you feel about the idea of writing beyond your own experience, and how difficult that is? People are accused of speaking for people rather than allowing people to speak for themselves, where would you weigh in on that?

LW: I just wouldn't weigh in on it. Do I mind if a man writes in a woman's voice? No. Do I mind if a straight person writes in a queer voice? No. I mind if they do it offensively. You know, I mind if I read and think '*really*?' So I guess, I mind the writing and the attitude and the politics. Could I write in the voice of a Japanese person? I don't think I could, because I don't have enough knowledge, but I wouldn't say that nobody else ever should. I don't like the idea that we close down, I think that we should be broadening out, and opening up. Stevie in my books is mixed race. Some readers might not even notice and that's fine as well, but I wanted

her to be a real Londoner, and London is a hugely multicultural place. Yeah – I understand the idea of appropriation and colonisation and I think people should be aware of and alert to it, and not just think 'yeah, this will be beautifully exotic' or anything. The idea of 'exoticism' I think is offensive.

RD: In 2014 you were involved with creating The Empire Cafe, which highlighted Glasgow's often suppressed involvement in the Atlantic slave trade. Since then how has that conversation progressed?

LW: Well, I don't really know. I guess Jude Barber (the other half of the Empire Café) and I made a contribution, but we drew on historians who were doing work already, James Robertson who had written his book already, Graham Fagan, Graham Campbell, Steven Mullen, all sorts of people. I think we helped broaden and open up the discussion, and I think we helped introduce people who might not otherwise have met, and that's quite exciting. I think we made a space which was welcoming while also being challenging, and we brought thousands of people in, we got some new stories commissioned, which went on Radio 4 and were heard by literally millions of people, so we don't know what comes from that – you just have to step back and wait and see. You can't quantify what you did and what other people do. I think that's the joy of collaboration. Jude and I did a thing last year as part of the Merchant City Festival, discussing museums and representation, and I guess that's where my attention has been drawn now. The conversation about our colonial past has been going on all across Scotland, but the question is what are we going to do about it? Do we have lesson plans in schools? When people go into the National Museum of Scotland what do they see about this aspect of our country's history? So that's where my focus is. I think there's an idea of a national story, but our sanctioned national story for the larger part doesn't acknowledge that we weren't always heroic, that we weren't always the underdog. I shouldn't say we, I mean the nation, the nation did rather well out of the British Empire. The other thing I think about is, when we discuss slavery, when we discuss this iniquity, we are discussing capitalism in its rawest form. What could be rawer than buying and selling, not just people, but their children, who might be the children of the person that's buying and selling them as well? It's mind-blowing – what could be rawer capitalism than that?

RD: If there is a consistent enemy in all your novels, a sort of Big Bad, it seems to be that idea of exploitation. Some of your heroes confront that evil, sometimes they defeat it, either in a small way or in a more significant way. What informs that?

LW: Gosh I don't know. I guess, I was brought up in a working-class household. Money wasn't the most important thing. Your job was your job, and your focus at home would be your family, some people would have hobbies and that would be their joy. So maybe it's that, maybe it's just thinking that while we need money to live, it's not really the most important thing. Although we all need

money because without it, you're sitting under Jamaica Bridge aren't you?

RD: In a similar vein, all of your protagonists, they seem to have an element of performance or creativity in their life, but often rubbing against commerce and earning a living. So you've got William Wilson in *The Bullet Trick* who's a stage magician and earns a living doing that, Murray Watson is an academic and a lecturer, so again there's a sort of element of performance but that's his living, Rilke is an auctioneer, of course, and in *The Girl on the Stairs* your main character is a bookseller. Is that your way of exploring your experience of being a writer, perhaps?

LW: It could be. Certainly, writing is a strange mix of creativity and commerce, isn't it, and especially right now. It's well-known how difficult it can be for writers who don't hit a certain level of sales. But I think it's probably always been like that. I believe passionately in subsidy for the arts, because without it there are voices we just don't hear. I've been lucky the last wee while I don't need a subsidy right now, but that day's in the post [laughs]. But it's not self-interest that drives this belief in supporting the arts in all their forms.

I'm fascinated with the world of work, while never really wanting a proper job myself. But I've always worked, I've always paid my taxes. You mentioned *The Girl on the Stairs*. Jane in *The Girl on the Stairs* is pregnant. She's one half of a same-sex couple. She and her partner are going to have this baby, part of the reason for Jane's isolation is that she's willingly given up her job. Her partner Petra is going to support her and the baby. Part of Jane's crisis is that she's now completely dependent on somebody else, and that is a precarious place to be.

RD: Does writing feel like a kind of grift, a sleight-of-hand.

LW: On the good days! [laughs] William Wilson, who you mentioned, is a stage magician. Prestidigitation is what we're aiming for with the book too, or the story or the play. When we go to see a magic show, everybody over the age of about five, or six, knows that magic doesn't exist, but we go in and we watch the show, and we're transported. We give ourselves over to the magician. Writing is like that as well, we know this is a story, but if it works and if we invest, and the writer does their job, we have a wonderful experience.

RD: I like the idea of sort of learning the tricks of the trade. Can you talk a little bit about that?

LW: There's things that you get better at, but you have to not be too slick. To keep the circus analogy, in every acrobatic trick there should be a moment where you think that somebody might fall. There should be a little wobble, or else it just looks too easy, and we just let it all glide over us. Visual artists are thinking about this as well. John Walters, a friend of ours, has a show on in Dundee, DCA, recently called Shonky. Technology enables some artists to create beautiful things, untouched by human hand in perfect fabrics, and yet somehow that can become unpleasing to the eye. We welcome evidence of the hand, a bit of shonkiness. The same can be true within

writing. Maybe that's why I'm attracted to genre writing – that's not to say that genre writing is any less worthy, or easier to do, but sometimes you see the hand of the maker in it, and I think that can be satisfying. I find it hard to say why. The thrill and the spill.

This on the table here, this is an libretto for a new opera called Anthropocene that I'm working on with composer Stuart MacRae, hich will have it's premier with Scottish opera in January 2019. I'm on the final scene and, oh my god, it must all fit. That it doesn't mean that everybody should understand every aspect of the show, but nobody should walk out of that theatre thinking 'what the fuck was that? I just didn't get it. I didn't understand it. That didn't work'. You can't ask for three hours of someone's life, and then not deliver. So yeah, getting better but still having an edge, I guess that's what I aspire to. Whether it always comes out like that is another question.

RD: Do some skills transfer from one type of writing to another? Do you have to get yourself into different modes of thinking for novels or libretti?

LW: Well, with something like opera, it's a great big team which starts off with you and the composer, and both of you must equally own this endeavour. Perhaps the aspect that transfers is story, story and characterisation, everybody must, to an extent, see the same people, so when I say the lead character is this, Stuart must also agree, he must feel that as well. You work on these characters, and you know what their voices are, and then that is transferred to the director, the designer. And the singers themselves must know it, and then hopefully the audience too. There has to be an integrity there, it all has to fit. The differences between genres is part of the joy, and the intellectual rigour, the exercise. It can be cleansing to go from a novel to something else. There's what, three, four-hundred pages in a novel, I think there's fifty in this libretto, which has taken a huge amount of time, but of course you're leaving space for other things, for the music, the acting, for the voices. In the book I might say – hopefully better than this – 'Prentice is feeling upset.' In a libretto, the music, the voice, and the acting tells us that she's upset. You know there really shouldn't be a point where she says 'I'm feeling upset', because that's not using the medium to the best advantage.

RD: How do you think about musicality when writing libretti?

LW: Stuart MacRae is so musically literate. I learn a lot from talking to him. Tone, mood, what the voices are, what the tempo is, the re-emergence of themes, so if you're a good listener you may hear something musically at a point in the opera that comes back later on and says 'remember that thing that happened there, remember that moment.' Or it may be the same theme but slightly upside down or inverted or in a different tone that says we're back in this territory. It's a joy to work on, but really bloody hard.

RD: You dedicated *No Dominion* to your agent David Miller, who died in 2016. Could you talk a little about the role of the agent, and particularly David Miller's role in your career.

LW: There are things you don't expect. David was great and David was somebody that was with myself, and with Zoë at the start of our careers. I thought that he would always be there, I imagined that I would go before David, actually, because he was more lively than me. It was a big shock. I guess the agent is there to do all sorts of things. The agent is connected in a way that the author often isn't. The agent is there to help you to an extent with the business side, to match you up perhaps with people that you wouldn't even know existed; to suggest possibilities. I edited a big anthology of one hundred ghost stories after David said to Head of Zeus publishers, 'Louise will do you a nice book of ghost stories, she'll hand it in on time and she'll enjoy it.' And I did, I loved it. That kind of thing. But an agent is also somebody who hopefully likes your work and knows your work, and will sit down with you with the text and say 'you know you always do that thing, take it out.' They're another mentor, somebody who knows your work intimately. All over the world there are people who were sad to see David go. Not only because of those things, but because he was such a nice person. I saw him a few days before he died, we sat down and worked on a book together, we went through it, and his marks were still on the page. I couldn't believe it when he died. He was also really good writer, and a very knowledgeable man. When someone leaves the world, all that knowledge leaves as well.

RD: *The Plague Times* trilogy was influenced by the Cold War. You've mentioned *Threads* and *Survivors* as references. You started writing the series in 2014 and four years later we now have Brexit, Trump, North Korea in the news, all these indications that we are living in a less secure and less stable world. Do you feel we are returning to a Cold War mentality and what's the writer's place in that new world?

LW: For the benefit of the tape: I am miming the Munch painting, 'The Scream.' Well I really had to work on the ending of that trilogy, because I am beginning to realise what a cyclical thing the world is. As a child I used to think society was evolutionary, that we became better people. That we get better. Perhaps that's what we're taught as children. And then you realise that we don't, we just get better toys. All the cavefolk had was a club, and now we've got these huge missiles. I am to my core anti-nuclear.

The novelist's role? Well the novelists are all individuals aren't they. You can only write what you can write. I'd love to write a great philosophical middle-European thing. But I can't do that. Somebody gets murdered, somebody cracks a joke. From the very beginning my books have always had a political spine running through them. Maybe it isn't always obvious: there's characters; there's jokes; there's sex, sometimes there's guns. But there is always politics at the heart of the text. None of them are manifestos, but they all have that spine to them. Which is maybe why *The Times* said I was a moraliser. And I said they were utter bastards.

RD: What's your next project. What are you excited about?

LW: I am excited about finishing the Libretto. Anthropocene hits the stage in January 2019 with Scottish Opera. And I've started a new book, I'm 15,000 words in. So will it work, or will it not? There's always excitement in that. At present it's a campus novel. It's exploring 21st century colonialism. And it's got the usual dose of sex and violence. Less sex and more violence as I get older – I think that's a worrying trend. I might try and up the sex content. You've got to keep the faith.

Golf Baws

Charles Lang

Armed wae a big strong club,
(a hof bottle, n a couple a cans a Tennents)
we'd take tae the bushes
fur golf baws.

In oor auld sannies, mind,
cos it's mucky,
n a jaiket
cos it might start pishin doon.

I'd watch n learn, wee man,
as he dug the club right in aboot
the jaggies tae get the wan
I couldnae reach.

He'd find yella wans, pink wans, blue wans,
green wans, Nike wans, even Scotland wans.
You name it –
aw in a hard day's graft.

I'd keep ma eyes peeled aw the wiy up
right tae the tap ae the Braes
where we'd coont thum
n launch aff the shiters n the pink wans.

We'd huv pieces
n I'd eat thum aw,
even the crusts,
like a big strong boy.

N we'd sit,
n we could see the swing park across fae ma granny's bit,
n then the drink would hit
n I lost him.

Litany

Colette O'Connor

looking for god / looking for god burning herbs in a flowerpot watching sparks puncture holes in the dark / looking for god in silence / in the soundlessness of snow / looking for god in the boughs of an ancient yew barefoot alone at night with a racing heart / looking for god held and caught in the twisting sinews of the ocean current singing / looking for god in a language i don't speak / looking for god in my loneliness / looking for god in the past in roots piercing strata pushing holy tendrils up through concrete / in the cold smell of stone / in the ribcage of the church ceiling the flank of a poor starved beast shivering from a touch / looking for god on wikipedia / looking for god in a library book which lists each cell of my heart as reasons for damnation in an neat san-serif font returning the library book and shutting my emptiness in the cupboard / looking for god in equality only to be told he doesn't live there / looking for god with blood smearing my thighs / looking for god in shadow-fingered codeine nightmares / looking for god in the face of an old woman smiling with unsettling calm / looking for god sitting in a damp overcoat in a room in glasgow gazing into an old white woman's so called third eye thinking is this a cult fuck i hope i haven't joined a cult / looking for god in the mountains with altitude sickness drunk off one pint crying at the moon / looking for god between bouts of vomiting / looking for god in the care of a sudden friend / looking for god in fire glinting primal off a silver door / looking for god with static in my knees / in smoke / in the smudged blue morning with the last stars dwindling / looking for god at the vanishing point the river surges toward carrying lamps marigolds shit and half-charred bones / looking for god along the pilgrimage path then running back away from a man masturbating / looking for god suicidal / looking for god suicidal and laughing / looking for god ankle deep in the sea laughing watching a pufferfish this spherical fish is a thing that exists it's absurd and laughing and still wanting to die / looking for god and finding a hollow ache / looking for god but too afraid to leave the house / looking for god in politics in solidarity in community / looking for god in (whose streets) our streets / looking for god holding hands with strangers as we bury our dead / looking for god in the wreckage of my shame / looking for god without hope of love / looking for god crying you could have found me first

Midnight Worker

David Ross Linklater

There's something comforting
in the sound of dishes
being washed late at night
when the garden is frozen.
It gives the world hope.
Every other light
on the building is out.
Just that one person
cleaning dishes
not talking, restoring
some regularity
to the order of things.
Knowing that someone
somewhere
is getting something done
and we're not all just
watching each other
letting it all crack up
with the moon lit
and the rats down
amongst the bins
is the only thing
holding tomorrow
back.

Intrinsic

Jay Whittaker

All I know
is there's a word
I've forgotten

I falter.
Tongue stalls,
loading...

Everyone stares

my lost word
dams the flow
they stare, dammit

I flounder
splashing word-water
'It begins with I...
It's when something is inside...'

Interloping words elbow to the front

integral   intellect
interned   integrity.

I am being stared at
as I do the shell
of my father, guttering
in his nursing home bed,
uttering aphasic nonsense –
except now, his words make sense.

'What has become
of my elusive control?'

Panic tastes metallic.

Does the motorway,
deserted at night
pine for cars?

Does it relish
taut, empty tarmac?

Blame home time on Friday,
my age, medication –

Breathe.
Be a river surging
round this stone.
Let me flow.

Let intrinsic go.

The Cutting Ring

Catherine Simpson

It started when Bob got the bricks. He brought them home every day, a few at a time. If I was round the back pegging out the washing he'd hold one up and say: 'They're good quality are these; Accrington brick,' and he'd stack them by the shed under the old oak tree.

When I asked him what they were for he'd light a fag and pretend he hadn't heard. He's never been a big talker has Bob.

Gradually the pile got bigger and when it reached his chest he said, yet again: 'You'd pay a good price for a stack of bricks like that.'

Bob was due to finish work after 40-odd years at the big house. Our yard and shed are full of stuff he has dragged back over the years – even if he's no earthly use for it.

When I asked him for the umpteenth time what the bricks were for, he said: 'Them bricks; they're the sort they used for the foundations of the Empire State Building.' I looked at him, so he said: '*And* Blackpool Tower,' like *that* drew a line under it.

He was always cheap, was Bob, which is why we've been stuck out here all these years.

We moved to this cottage when we were first married; the rent was six shillings a week for the back bedroom and as much cold water as we could use. There was no central heating, no fitted kitchen, no fitted carpets, no neighbours, no buses, no streetlights; no life. Bob's dad came as a fixture and fitting.

He was even less fun than Bob.

I wonder how many hours I've spent washing pots and rinsing clothes at the back kitchen sink, watching my wedding ring sink into the flesh on my left hand, cutting right in, so I can't take it off now even when I try. How many hours I've stared through the window watching that oak tree change with the seasons?

I never learned to drive. Bob said it was too dear. 'What do you want with driving?' He said. 'I can run you to the shops.'

He takes me to town every other Saturday in his van. It's quick sharp round the butchers, the bakers and the candle-stick makers and straight home.

The day after Bob retired my heart sank. He was up at half six as usual, had his porridge and stood, with his hands on his hips, staring at that pile of bricks. I said: 'Why don't you build a wall' – although that was stupid – why would he build a wall? 'Or a barbecue,' I said. 'Why don't you build a barbecue?' He looked at me like I was daft and said: 'A barbecue? What would I want one of them for?' I said: 'For frying sausages,' and he said: 'You've got a frying pan, haven't you?'

I was surprised when he set to and started to dig a hole. At first I thought it might be a fish pond; some Koi carp or something for his retirement, but then I remembered Koi carp cost money. Goldfish, then? But he kept on digging, deeper and deeper, wider and wider until the hole was over eight feet deep and eight feet wide and it looked like a great big elephant trap.

Then he started lining the hole with the bricks; folding the cement mix and the sand into the water with his spade, tamping it down over and over like he was mesmerised. I watched him from the kitchen window and wondered if he'd lost his mind now that he had no job to go to, and was stuck here all day.

He had a spirit level and kept checking everything was straight. He was very particular. One day when he was asleep in his armchair, I went outside and I had a good look in the hole. There were two raised bits – like shelves – one on either side. I stared at them for ages.

Then one night he said the old oak tree had roots that might interfere with his brickwork. I could see him thinking about those roots travelling underground, where he couldn't see them or control them.

The next day he was brushing the sides of the big brick hole with a wire brush to make them smooth. I was pegging out sheets and I asked him what he was building, although I didn't expect an answer. He straightened up. 'It's for us,' he said. 'Me here and you over there.' I walked to the edge of the hole and looked inside. I stared at the smooth red-brick shelf on either side it, and it was *then* I realised what he was making.

It was a crypt, a tomb, for the both of us; so we could be together for ever and ever, till kingdom come, Amen. And not even in the churchyard where there might be a bit of company, no, here, in the garden of this cottage. Just the two of us.

Bob carried on brushing and smoothing and making it perfect. I couldn't say a word. I saw how small it was; how enclosed, how neat. How final.

He hadn't even asked me.

This morning I took out some seeds for the birds. I was filling the feeder that hangs from the oak tree when something caught my eye. I reached up and felt the trunk and found a copper wire tied so tight round the trunk that it was sunk deep into the bark and had cut the bark right through, all the way round; so the sap couldn't rise. I touched it, for seconds or it could have been minutes or hours. It felt like forever.

I looked up at the branches whispering overhead, and I knew no matter what I did for the oak tree, there was no saving it now. Its leaves would wither and fade and blow away, and its roots would stop wandering and never crack Bob's perfect brickwork. The tree would die because the copper ring was tied too tight and had sunk in too deep. I couldn't get the ring off if I tried – and even if I could it wouldn't make any difference now.

Because it was all too late.

Endangered

Melanie Henderson

She'd owned twenty-six coats.

Natalie learns this when her grandmother dies.

She goes to help her mother clear out the sheltered flat and they haul everything out of the wardrobe, laying the coats on the bed. When they're nearly done, it looks as if there must be a wild party going on in another room, full of beautiful, eccentric women. Natalie imagines heavy, floral perfume, spirals of smoke from menthol cigarettes, lipstick kisses on cut glass.

There are raincoats and tailored jackets, sheepskins and leathers, brocades and tweeds. Rainbow colours. Fabrics you want to feel.

There's a baby pink jacket with oversize buttons, Jackie Kennedy style. Tiny, fit for a doll. She shrugs on a satin blazer, red, with oriental embroidery, but it won't fasten. The hormones have been playing havoc with her weight.

All morning, they've cleared cupboards, wrapped ornaments in newspaper, packed cutlery and plates. Frances had been a hoarder. In the hall cupboard, they found fifteen multipacks of toilet roll. The kitchen revealed eighteen tins of beans. The drawers were stuffed with packets of biscuits, some of them open and growing mould.

'She must have been stockpiling for nuclear winter,' said Natalie's mother, Rosemary.

They'd each taken one or two things they liked: Rosemary took a rose-patterned tea-set, missing one saucer; Natalie chose a blue glass cockerel she thought she might have given to Frances when she was small.

'You do know that's only got one eye?' Rosemary said.

'I know. I just like it,' said Natalie.

The wardrobe was last to be emptied. So far, she's recognised only two of the coats: a navy wool, for winter, and a beige Mac with a tartan lining. On the bed are versions of her grandmother she didn't know.

'She always liked her clothes,' Rosemary says. 'Probably compensating for all that making do after the war.'

At the back of the rail is a green zip-lock bag with the Harrods logo in gold. Natalie lifts it out; it's bulky and heavy. She lays it flat, unzips it, inch by inch, as if whatever's in there might give her a fright. 'Wow,' she says.

She drags out a long-length fur, trimmed in brown leather, lined in black silk. It's real: so plush it might have just come off the animal.

'Very glam,' says her mother.

Natalie strokes the pelt and shudders. 'Poor beast,' she says. Her degree's in environmental science; she's been vegetarian for years.

'Well, you can't resuscitate it now,' says Rosemary. 'Isn't leopard in again?'

'As long's it's fake. Though that's just as bad. Massive carbon footprint.'

'But they stopped all that throwing paint on people years ago.'

'Yeah, but wearing it just makes it okay again.'

Rosemary sighs. 'Charity pile, then. Shame.' She wets a finger, opens another bin liner and hands it to Natalie.

'Nope. Charity shops won't touch them. You can't even flog them on eBay. It's illegal. It's because it's endangered.' She puts her face to the coat: just the chemical whiff of mothballs; a faint fustiness underneath. 'Although now we're just ruining their habitat.'

Her mother ruffles the fur. 'So what do we do with it?'

'Homeless shelter, maybe? Animal rights groups sometimes use them for education. Or a museum.'

She thinks of the coat in a glass display case, on a bald and faceless fibreglass mannequin, with those awful, rigid hands. She grimaces. 'No. Too creepy.'

She has a flash of Frances, arms open, at the end of a long, thin corridor; her old house in the town centre. The plastic floor runner makes a noise like a slurp as Natalie runs towards her. Her grandmother is warm and soft; the flour from her apron goes up Natalie's nose. The kitchen has pale yellow units. A big, oval table, scored on the top, laden with sandwiches. Scones cooling on a rack. Bramble jelly in a china pot.

She sits down on the pile of coats; Rosemary sits too and Natalie budges over and takes her hand.

After a while, she gets up and zips the fur back into its sleeve.

She says, 'I'll take it. I'll think of something to do with it.'

Later, at her mother's house, she runs her finger over her nose, tracing its curve and swoop: a bit less severe with each generation. Thank God she isn't going to be passing it on.

'She bequeathed me this,' she says, pinching her nostrils. 'Cheers, gran.'

Rosemary touches her own nose. 'It's a fine feature, I'll have you know.'

They've unloaded the car, stashing the boxes and bags in the spare room. They'll have to do one more trip, at least. Now they sit with their coffee at the window, looking over St Andrews harbour; the sunset is coral and grey with a flare of yellow. Natalie tastes onions from the chow mein they ordered; there's a film of grease on her lips. She undoes the button on her waist band and feels her stomach relax. She thinks of the marks there: red needlepoints in a semi-circle; a little constellation. But they're starting to fade.

Twenty-six coats and a whole lot of crockery. It isn't much.

Frances encouraged her to knit – through and off, through and off – making circular gestures with her hand. When Natalie held up her work, honeycombed with dropped stitches, Frances would fix it; lightning needles that should have sparked. Because of her, she knows the best way to sew on a button – three firm stitches through the material first – and how to test whether jam is ready by putting a spoonful on a cold plate and letting it run; if it ripples, it's set.

She doesn't do any of those things anymore; she hasn't done them since she was small.

She casts a glance at Rosemary: she's aged well, but her cheeks are pinched in now and there's a web of blue veins at her neck. Natalie has a picture of the three of them in her wallet, taken about fifteen years ago. Frances in the middle, rouge lifting her cheeks, white hair newly rinsed with silver. Rosemary, still with her auburn, before she stopped the dye. Her own hair, shiny and full; face almost plump. She crosses her legs and notices her shorts aren't quite long enough to hide the pocked flesh on her thighs.

'D'you know what I wish?' she says. She takes a gulp of coffee and leans back in her chair. 'I wish she'd taught me to iron.' She breathes deeply, conjuring puffs of hot steam, lemon-smelling from the fabric softener. Her grandmother at work, pressing, folding. Doing shirts like origami. So perfect, it seemed a crime for anyone to wear them again.

'I thought you were proud of never ironing anything,' Rosemary says. 'I'd have shown you, but I always thought you were happy with your books.'

'I was. Mostly. But it's like magic, isn't it? A clean, fresh pile of ironing.' She shrugs. 'Maybe it's a gene that skipped a generation.'

'Ha,' says Rosemary. 'It's a dying art, isn't it? Same as all those things. Used to be they were survival skills. Changed days.'

'What I need is an ironing bot.'

Rosemary shakes her head. 'Don't think I want to hang around for all that.'

'It won't be all machines. There'll be changes to humans. Babies of the future will get an extra limb that doubles as a selfie stick.'

Her mother laughs. 'Survival of the fittest?'

'Maybe. Though who knows where it'll end up. It's like the gazelles learning to jump higher and higher to put off the cheetahs. There's only so high they can go. Then they'll have to adapt all over again.'

The sun has dipped right down now. Sooty clouds mushroom over the harbour. The water is glossy and dark.

Natalie knows without turning to look that Rosemary is studying her, probably frowning.

'You know when I had you they thought I was ancient,' she says. Her voice is quiet, light. 'Elderly primigravida.'

'Yes. You were a total dinosaur.'

I'm sorry to tell you it's negative.

The call came last week. The voice firm, professional.

She'd held it together, polite: *Thanks so much for letting me know quickly.*

She isn't sure what's worse: grim reality or false hope. 'Mum, seriously,' she says.

'There's a bit of a difference between twenty-eight and forty-five. Biology is smart, but not that smart. And don't say it.'

'What?'

'That miracles happen.'

Rosemary raises a hand, apologetic. 'But you never know. Nature sometimes finds a way.'

Natalie snorts and puts her coffee cup down on the windowsill. There's a pale skin on the top. She puts her finger through it and a dark hole expands.

She drives home to Perth with the leopard coat on the parcel shelf. It's so big it partly obscures the rear view. In the driver's mirror, her eyes are ringed blue.

In the morning, before she left to pick up her mother, he'd wanted to go over it all again. For God's sake, she said. Not now. It wasn't as if it was the only thing on her mind.

Okay, Steve said. It wasn't the right time. It was just he couldn't stand it, all the tension, the silence. Maybe after the dust had settled. After the funeral. If it was the money that was bothering her, he'd worked out a way. She said it wasn't. It wasn't him who had to inject himself or lie with his legs up in stirrups, like something from a farm. He said it wasn't as if he'd had much fun with his plastic cup, either.

She hates driving in the dark. She shouldn't have stayed so long at her mother's. Her contacts dance on her eyes, making bright pools; the headlights coming towards her leave contrails of orange. A lorry driver dips too late and she swerves in the white shock, tyres juddering on cat's eyes.

He'd just kept on.

It's just we've got so much to give.

I still see us with a child.

It's not as if I wasn't going through it too.

We can do this.

Yadda, yadda, yadda.

As for work, he said if she really thought the council's environmental policy team was going to fall apart without her, he'd take a sabbatical. He was pretty sure the geography department could stand a crazy supply teacher for a few terms.

She goes to overtake and the car in front of her moves out, without indicating. She thumps her hand on the horn.

She'd been waiting for the result when she'd last seen Frances. She was picturing a ball of cells, dividing and multiplying; by now, it would look like the inside of a pomegranate. She was thinking this as she squeezed the old lady's hand. Frances was sparrow-like, hoarse with the pain. The hospital sheet was barely rising. They were just keeping her comfortable now, the nurses said. It wouldn't be all that long. Comfortable, she thought. What a joke. There was terror in her grandmother's eyes.

Just one last shot. One more and that's it.

She'd ended up shouting.

When are you going to fucking realise? It's not as if we're dying out as a species. We're over-running the fucking planet. We're wiping out the animals. And after them, it's us. The sixth mass extinction is just around the corner. We're not that important. This isn't our right.

And she saw him clench his teeth, but he didn't shout back. In a flat, careful voice he said she could use her environmental conscience as an excuse if she wanted. But there was nothing wrong with being scared.

She said that had nothing to do with it.

She whispers it now, head nearly on the windscreen as she negotiates the dark. 'Not scared. I'm not.'

There are roadworks ahead and the carriageway narrows to a single lane. Her full beam is on but she has to slow right down to see her way through the chicane marked by reflective barriers.

Having no fear. That would be a thing.

Like being eleven. On the dodgems at a fairground. Screaming and swerving. The electric conductor sizzling above. High on candy floss and toffee apples.

Frances had watched her from the crash barrier. Natalie turned and waved, and in that second she was hit full-on. Her forehead smacked the steering wheel, hard plastic that felt like stone. She cried out, but managed to sit up; the boy in the other dodgem grinned and yanked the wheel round to turn his car away. An attendant rushed over and then Frances was there too. The red sparks from the ceiling hovered like fireflies.

There's a car on her tail now; the driver flashes his lights but she ignores it, her foot nudging the brake.

Frances had run to the butcher's to fetch a bag of ice. It helped, but there was still an enormous bump on her forehead. Frances told her it was blue, like a duck egg. She put her hand up to feel it; she was so proud.

Back on dual carriageway, Natalie runs her fingertips over a spot just above her right eye. It's smooth and cool. She squeezes the accelerator.

Steve had put on his teacher voice.

It's one baby. It's not as if we'll be solely responsible for the end of the natural world. And if we don't have one, it doesn't mean we've saved it, either.

She started up again, but he stopped her. Told her she could keep the speech.

Her neck aches and she shakes out her shoulders. Now, she just wants to get home.

She finds him in the kitchen with a bottle of Merlot. He has a novel open, but she can tell he isn't reading.

He looks up, takes his glasses off. His eyes are bleary. His chin is shadowed with growth.

'Was it grim?' he says.

'A bit.'

He gets another glass and fills it to the brim.

'Turns out she used to be a real fashionista. The Imelda Marcos of the coat world.'

The wine tastes of brambles; the tannins cling like tobacco at the back of her throat.

She shows him the coat and tells him she doesn't know why she's kept it. It's awful, really.

'No!' he says. 'Amazing!'

He wants her to try it on. 'Go on. Just the once.' He holds it up against her, tickles her face with it.

'No,' she says, shoving him back. 'I'm not ditching my principles just to indulge your wee fantasy.'

'Please,' he says. 'Pretty please. I won't tell anyone.' He holds her close and rubs her nose with his.

'Is this some sort of weird mating ritual?' she says.

'Maybe. You never know your luck.'

She caves in and slides her arms into the silk lining. 'I hope you know I'm not enjoying this.'

'I appreciate it.'

It's so heavy, she nearly overbalances. It hangs almost to her feet, brushing her ankles. The feel of it, so soft and lavish, is thrilling; she has to stifle a little sigh.

'Wow,' he says. 'It was made for you.' He puts his hands on her shoulders and strokes to her wrists.

'Let's see, then.' She goes to the full-length mirror in the hall.

'Bloody hell.' She turns sideways on. 'Reckon I wouldn't be out of place down Leith docks.'

'I'd pick you up,' he says. 'If I was looking. Which I wouldn't be. Obviously.'

'Well, thanks very much. I'm flattered.'

'You're gorgeous,' he says.

'Yeah, right.'

'No,' he says. 'I mean it.'

He takes her face in his hands.

There's hardly anyone at the funeral; she can't believe it.

'Guess that happens when you're ninety-five,' Steve says. 'Mourners get thin on the ground.'

Natalie sits in the front pew between Steve and her brother, Robert, up from London. Rosemary is perched next to Robert, her right thumb drawing circles in her left hand.

The eulogy is a cut-and-paste affair. There'll be websites for that, Natalie thinks, like the ones that sell essays. The minister met Frances just once, when she was dying. He says it was a long life, a happy one, and that she lived for her family and friends. He refers to Rosemary as Rosie; Natalie sees her flinch. He drops his notes. Stammers over dates and facts he's never seen.

The Lord is My Shepherd is a poor effort: no one seems to know the new version of the tune, which isn't the one Rosemary picked, and there aren't enough people to carry it; it comes out all whispery, embarrassed. The organist hits a bum note and the whole thing just about falls apart, but they get to the end, and sit.

'Christ,' whispers Steve and she elbows him in the ribs. He mouths, 'Sorry.'

At the graveside, Natalie has to take a cord. She tries not to look into the dreadful trench; she feels the chill of it beneath her.

Something goes wrong – maybe it's her who doesn't let go as she's supposed to – and the coffin stalls, bashing the walls of the grave. She feels a terrible pull and lurches forwards. One of the undertakers looks ready to step in, but then the rope slides through her fingers and the casket bumps its way into the pit.

She doesn't cry. She squeezes the tissue in her pocket, bites down on her bottom lip.

The wind is whipping up and she crosses her arms around herself, watching black overcoats drift towards cars. She's stupidly worn heels, which have sunk into the mud, like tent pegs.

They drive to the golf club, where her grandfather used to be a member, and eat white triangles stuffed with egg and cress; the egg is going slightly green. The white wine is good, though; it tastes of gooseberries and grass. She guzzles three big glasses. Her brother goes to the bar and brings back Sambuca.

She goes outside on her own and the cold air is like a blow. She sits on the wall, head to her knees; she belches aniseed and acid wine, smells the half-digested egg. Then she heaves everything up, splattering her shoes in thick, yellowish vomit.

Steve is there. His hand is on her back. He sits on the wall and holds her forehead.

'That's it,' he says. 'Let it all come up.' When she's sick again, he just gets his feet out of the way in time.

After she's drunk some water and cleaned herself up with peach hand wash, they sit until she feels she can cope with the car journey. She's clammy and her hair sticks to her face.

She cries, then, quietly. He finds her a fresh tissue and she blows her nose.

She takes both his hands.

'Okay,' she says. 'Let's do it.'

He starts to say something, but she puts a finger to his lips.

He pushes a strand of hair back from her brow.

She means to do something with the leopard coat, but in the months that follow it hangs at the back of the closet, forgotten.

The clothes rail collapses and Steve says it's probably the weight of the coat; he fixes it, putting in extra screws, but it happens again, so the zip-lock bag is left in the bottom of the wardrobe, along with dresses and jumpers Natalie has bagged for charity and then abandoned.

Sometime later, the coat manages to escape its bag; it stretches itself right out, settling over odd shoes, old boxes and broken umbrellas.

And it stays there, hiding in the dark, like the animal it once was.

An Old Woman

Kevin Williamson

There's an old woman hanging
round the courts each morning
the tattered suits & stale bravado
the wee lassies & the hard men
smoking cigarettes by the pack.
She talks waits nods her head
crushes doups into her palms
grown as hard as wingnut bark.
She's not that old 45 perhaps
lips pursed into a resignation
a faith a protective morality
her only son a good boy really
led astray drunk an accident.
You can never tell with judges
they don't live in the real world
Jack says they're all paedophiles
in wigs whispers of a magic circle.
One foot shuffles to the other
picks hair from an old fur coat
checks her watch turns this way
that dabs her eye must be dust.
Half past light from an older sun
her wee boy cheeky back then
nothing bad first day at school
full of it he was made her laugh.
He could've been killed thon time
fell off his trike under the wheels
of a milk truck fractured his skull
a right handful broke his collarbone.
Laid up in hospital for six months.
Lucky it wisnae a beer lorry eh?
The doctor said aye right enough.
That's whit she didnae understand
must have known what it felt like
the brutal crunch of metal on bone

a desperate cry for his old mammy
to comfort him make it all better.
An old woman checks her watch
time running out. A short sentence?

        Cannae dae the time?
        Dinnae dae the crime.

That's whit her Jack had eywis said.
No that she saw much of him between
spells inside & spells inside some hoor
aye once the whisky weaved its magic
a charmer Jack was when he wanted
to be everyone said so the life & soul.
Rocknroll nights at the club? Aw aye!
Piled her blonde hair up to a beehive
Jack greased to a slickback Elvis P.
Revivalists he would say the best sort.
Took her all the next day to revive him.
Bus hame through aw the usual haunts
Silver Wing stopping off at the Plaza
bread milk lottery paper for the telly.
Her wee boy looked smart in his suit
creaseless shirt proper knot in his tie
he looked over to her smiled at her
a wee bit glaikit but he smiled at her.
It was a long time since she'd seen him
smile at her used to have such a happy
wee face aw the neighbours said so
eywiz smiling that's what they said.
He'd need smokes & a top-up card for
his phone were they allowed phones?
Jack's big mate said he'd put a word in
make sure naebody took a lend of him.
They'd see him alright could be a while
all alone scared away from his mammy
she'd be there on the dot for every visit
sell everything the whole lot jewellery
flatscreen telly aw the rocknroll records
for one wee cuddle from her boy now.
He wisnae a bad lad no like the beasts
& the nonces & drug dealers & rapists.

Was an accident he was drunk led astray.
It could have happened to anyone.

Comrade

Ross Wilson

A Tory and a Royalist, Tam
was always welcome in the mining club
among men who saw him as a man
then a daft bastard, but only then,
for if Tam voted against the interests of his own
it wasn't because he was mean.

He'd have done anything for anyone
and never viewed a human being as vermin
unlike some champions of Socialism
who'd turn dictator in their own home;
women and bairns cowed to the God, Dad.
Tory, Royalist, not the brightest,

Tam was one of the best.
They called him Comrade.

Aye here

Hamish Scott

Thaim burn the carlines seeks thaim yit
Thaim gaird the daith camps wants thaim new
As faimlie, friens an neibours bides
Aye here amang us, me an you

Licht

Hamish Scott

Whiles A lik a lowin licht
tae redd awa the gowstie mirk;
whiles A lik a cannle flam
tae flichter i the enless dirk

The Bourtree

Sara Clark

An when, acause o men, yon Bourtree dee'd,
The smaw air o mornin hauntit it wi grief –
An the warld broch oot its daurk yairns then,
As the dowie sun shane caumly oan,
Its seilie ee sae clase tae clasin.

An suin, thae bluims that fillt the meidaes aince
Wis swallaed bi the laund's fell hunger,
An the wind that liltit lang in the birlin dust
Wis a wird awa fae the end o sang foriver.

An when the woundit widlaunds drapt at last,
An the rain plashed doun in draigs alang the villas,
Till e'en the bracky bree wis dicht asinder;
Ony then did oor ee'n sweel app in wunner,
As men, an beasts, and leafs, aw fell thegither.

Insomniac

Sara Clark

Shaidae o a dream,
Mirk-daurk alang the gowd-reid edge o ma vision
Faur as the watter's end,

Saft as the mooths o mist that slaik the stream
In lost collision,
Hou did ye set an ocean here? Hou did ye send

The unpossible vizzie? The ghaist-sea, glentin green?
Shoud ah envision
A boat as licht as amber, un-cleek it, an ascend

Thae scaudin, yellae waves
Alane throu the dreich black smoke o ma ain terror?
Tell us: for whase sake

Maun ah raik these aizelt shorelines tae the caves
Or be the beirer
O a bale that birns the sockets? Wha will take

Ma airm an lead me saftly frae this muntain o graves?
Ye hiv come nearer.
Whan will ah faw asleep? Whan will ah wake?

Ariadne

Sara Clark

He wis ma bevie,
Ilk glance a gowd glassfu,
a skyrie infeenity o us

The gless o the heivens
wis hale in my hauns an
fair fousome wi aw that he wis.

If this lyfe wis my ain yin
Ah'd gie it aw ower
Tae jyne him yince mair in the bour

Ma ee'n in the wine gless
Hae chynged intae his
an the wine is ableizin wi pouer.

The Kaelpie, the Wordis an the Roun-trie

Lindsey Shields Waters

Slawlye it gaynis forme. Twentye-sevyn
Pageis — giffyng trew accompt o hapnyngis
An wrangnys, strekyn rycht bak ty chyldheid.
Hyr wyreid pene lyis on the tabill an wachyn
Snaw cloudis ower-spyn skye, sche knawys
It's tyme. Outsycht, ane thrie ynch mantyll
O snaw, stille crysþ, coverys the sey path.

Na evydens o lyfe. Schill blastys dryve alle
Insycht. Nott ewyn redewyngs' rattill braks
Silens. Sche pullis on woll sokes, hevy butis
An wrappis hyr warmyst coyte tycht. Plasis
The wordis in ane ledder bage, grippis ane
Roun-trie branche in the ither hande. It's a
Fayre distans bot thare's na rusche. Standyn

Quyetlie bye wattir's eyge, sche waytys. The
Kaelpie wyl appeir lukin fore fuid. Ane storme
Bylds, ʒowlyng an draggyn its teythe thru pyne,
Birk an aik treis. Sche wantis ty heir the sowne
O the kaelpie's tayle — smel sault on its mane.
The sey's bak is vp, wawys hich. Lyk thunnyr
Swellowyn vp hyr breyth, it's clos. Sche drawis

Hyr coyte tychter as the kaelpie outisch frome
Sey in ane grete leip. Roun-trie branche alaft,
Standyn fyrm agaynys hym, sche stares intyll
ʒalow eyen. Hotte stynk o decepcioun. Foule
Injustis o anither's dethe. Nott me, sche cryis,
Slyngin the bage undyr the kaelpie's brydill.
Tak thys, lyk the reste o yer praye, deyp ty

The occeane bedd. Gorge on it wele vntyll it's
Na moyr. Pwrge me o trubilis an endles famyle
Fychtis. The kaelpie reirs its angerie heid, nek

Vaynis wreithyng, eyen flittyn atween roun-trie
Branche an the sey. Bailfullie it dyves vnta blak.
Sche's allane on the shoare, sey cawme; at pes.
Hyr paſt nowe sikkyr — twa baddis resolvyt.

The Upright Revolution (or Why Humans walk upright)

Da Upricht Revolution (or Why Humans traivel upricht)

Ngũgĩ wa Thiong'o translated into Shetlandic by Christine De Luca

A long time ago humans used to walk on legs and arms, just like all the other four limbed creatures. Humans were faster than hare, leopard or rhino. Legs and arms were closer than any other organs: they had similar corresponding joints: shoulders and hips; elbows and knees; ankles and wrists; feet and hands, each ending with five toes and fingers, with nails on each toe and finger. Hands and feet had similar arrangements of their five toes and finger from the big toe and thumb to the smallest toes and pinkies. In those days the thumb was close to the other fingers, the same as the big toe. Legs and arms called each other first cousins.

They helped each other carry the body wherever it wanted to go; the market, the shops, up and down trees and mountains, anywhere that called for movement. Even in the water, they worked well together to help the body float, swim or dive. They were democratic and egalitarian in their relationship. They could also borrow the uses of the product of other organs, say sound from mouth, hearing from the ear, smell from the nose, and even sight from the eyes. Their rhythm and seamless coordination made the other parts green with envy. They resented

Awa back in time fock ösed ta traivel apön baith legs an airms, jöst da sam as aa da idder fowr-limbed craiters. Humans wis faster as a hare, leopard or rhino. Legs an airms wis mair cosh as ony idder organs, joints braally muckle da sam: shooders an hench-banes; elbucks an knees; cöts an shacklebanes; feet an haands, ivery een endin in five taes an fingers, wi nails apön ivery tae an finger. Haands an feet hed der five fingers or taes set oot da sam, fae da muckle tae an toom tae da peeriest tae an peeriest finger. Danadays da toom wis clos tae da tidder fingers, sam as da muckle tae. Legs an airms coontit kin wi een anidder. Dey wir sib.

Dey helpit een anidder carry da boady whaarivver hit wantit ta geng; da market, da shops, up an doon trees an braes, whaarivver mövin aboot wis needit. Even i da watter, dey wirkit weel tagidder ta keep da boady aflot, ta help hit sweem an dive. Dey took accoont o een anidder's needs. Dey wir equals. Besides dat, dey wir able ta borrow da laeks o soond fae da mooth, hearin fae da lug, smell fae da neb, an even sicht fae da een. Da rhythm an da semless wye airms an legs wirkit tagidder med da tidder pairts o da boady envious. Dey wirna plaesed dat dey hed ta

having to lend their special genius to the cousins. Jealousy blinded them to the fact that legs and hands took them places. They started plotting against the two pairs.

Tongue borrowed a plan from Brain and put it to action immediately. It begun to wonder, loudly, about the relative powers of arms and legs. Who was stronger, it wondered. The two cousin limbs, who had never been bothered by what the other had and could do, now borrowed sound from mouth and begun to claim they were more important to the body than the other. This quickly changed into who was more elegant; arms bragged about the long slim fingers of its hands, at the same time making derisive comments about toes being short and thick. Not to be outdone, toes countered and talked derisively about thin fingers, starving cousins! This went on for days, at times affecting their ability to work together effectively. It finally boiled down to the question of power; they turned to other organs for arbitration. It was Tongue who suggested a contest. A brilliant idea, all agreed. But what? Some suggested a wrestling match – leg and arm wrestling. Others came up with sword play, juggling, racing, or playing a game like chess or checkers but each was ruled out as hard to bring about or unfair to one or the other limb. It was Tongue once again, after borrowing thought from Brain, who came with simple solution. Each set of organs would come up with a challenge, in turns. Arms and legs agreed.

The contest took place in a clearing in the forest, near a river. All organs were on maximum alert for danger or anything that might catch the body by surprise, now

lend der speeshil abilities tae der cooshins. Jeelousy blinndit dem tae da fact dat legs an haands took dem places. Dey stertit ta plot fornenst da twa pair o limbs.

Tongue tiggit a plan fae Brain an pat hit ta wirk richt awa. Hit began ta winder, oot lood, comparin da pooers o airms an legs; whit een o dem wis da maist bördly. Da twa limbs, sae clos an sib, wis nivver buddered afore bi whit da tidder een hed or could dö. But noo dey borrowed soond fae Mooth an began ta mak a wark dat dey wir mair ös tae da boady as da tidder limb. Dis shön changed inta whit een o dem wis boannier; airms braggit aboot da lang, slim fingers o der haands, at da sam time skyimpin da stubby taes. No ta be ootdön, da taes traepit an med a föl o da tin fingers; fantin cooshins! Dis gud on for days, sometimes makkin hit hard ta wirk weel tagidder. At last hit cam doon tae da question o pooer; dey luikit tae da tidder organs ta discern. Hit wis Tongue at suggestit a contest. Dey aa agreed his wis a graet idee. But whit? Some tocht a wrestlin match – leg an airm wrestlin. Idders cam up wi da idee o sword play, jugglin, racin, or playin a game like chess or chequers; but ivery een wis ruled oot as awkwird ta organise or unfair to wan o da limbs. Eence mair hit wis Tongue, eftir borrowin tocht fae Brain, at wirkit oot a simple answer. Each set o organs, takkin turns, wid mak up a challenge. Airms an legs agreed.

Da contest took place in a clearin in da forest, near a burn. Aa da organs wis on a amp, watchin fur danger or onythin dat micht, unlippened, gie da boady a bit o a gluff, noo dat hits organs wis set fornenst een anidder. Da een skiled far an wide fur da

that its organs were engaged in internal struggle. Eyes scanned far and wide for the tiniest of dangers from whatever distance; ears primed themselves to hear the slightest sound from whatever distance; nose cleared its nostrils the better to detect scent of any danger that escaped the watchful eyes and the listening ears; and the tongue was ready to shout and scream, danger.

Wind spread news of the contest to the four corners of the forest, water and air. Four legged animals were among the first to gather, many of the big ones holding green branches to show they came in peace. It was a colorful crowd of Leopard, Cheetah, Lion, Rhino, Hyena, Elephant, Giraffe, Camel, long horned Cow and short-horned Buffalo, Antelope, Gazelle, Hare, Mole and Rat. Water-Dwellers, Hippo, Fish, Crocodile, spread their upper part on the banks, leaving the rest in the river. The two leggeds, Ostrich, Guinea-fowl, and Peacock flapped their wings in excitement; birds chirped from the trees; Cricket sang all the time. Spider, Worm, Centipede, Millipede crawled on the ground or trees. Chameleon walked stealthily, carefully, taking its time while Lizard ran about, never settling down on one spot. Monkey, Chimpanzee, Gorilla, jumped from branch to branch. Even the trees and the bush, swayed gently from side to side, bowed, and then stood still in turns.

Mouth opened the contest with a song:

We do this to be happy
We do this to be happy
We do this to be happy

mintiest o dangers fae whitivver distance; lugs prunkit up ta lö tae da peeriest soond fae whitivver distance; da neb sneenit sae as hit could aesily niff ony danger da een wisna seen or da lugs heard; an da tongue wis ready ta screch an shout danger.

Wind spread da uncans o da contest tae da fowr coarners o da forest, watter an air. Fowr-leggit craiters were among da first ta gadder, a lok o da big eens haddin green branches ta shaa at dey cam in paece. Hit wis a glorius gadderie o Leopard, Cheetah, Lion, Rhino, Hyena, Elephant, Giraffe, Camel, lang-hoarn Kye an short-hoarn Buffalo, Antelope, Gazelle, Hare, Mole, Rat. Dem at bade athin watter – Hippo, Fysh, Crocodile – med a flatshie apö da burn-bank, sae dey could be haaf in an haaf oot o da watter. Dem wi jöst twa legs – Ostrich, Guinea-fowl an Peacock – flaachtered der wings, uploppm; birds chirpit fae da trees, Cricket nivver löt up singin. Speeder, Wirm, Creepy Craalies wi aa yon legs arled apö da grund or up da trees. Chameleon smootit, traivelled peeriewyes, while Lizard scuttered aboot, nivver at paece. Monkey, Chimpanzee, Gorilla loupit fae branch ta branch. Even da trees an da bush swayed a coarn fae side ta side, booed, an dan stöd still in turns.

Mooth stertit da contest wi a sang:

We dö dis ta be blyde
We dö dis ta be blyde
We dö dis ta be blyde
Fur we aa
Come fae wan natir.

Airms an Legs swör dey wid accept whitivver cam ta be, an no mak a wark o

Because we all
Come from one nature.

Arm and Legs swore to accept the outcome gracefully; no tantrums, threats of boycott, strikes or go-slow.

Arms issued the first challenge: they threw a piece of wood on the ground. The leg, left or right, or in combination, was to pick up the piece of wood from the ground and throw it. The two legs could consult each other, at any time in the contest, and deploy their toes, individually or collectively, in any order to effect their mission. They tried to turn it over; push it; they tried all sorts of combinations but they could not pick it up properly: and as for moving it, the best they could do was kick it a few inches away. Seeing this, Fingers borrowed sounds from the mouth and laughed, and laughed. Arms, the challenger, paraded themselves, as in beauty contest, showing off their slim looks, and then in different combinations picked the piece of wood. They threw it far into the forest, eliciting a collective sigh of admiration from the contestants and spectators. They displayed other skills: they picked tiny pieces of sand from a bowl of rice; they threaded needles; they made little small pulleys for moving heavier wood; made some spears and threw them quite far, moves and acts that the toes could only dream about. Legs could only sit there and marvel at the display of dexterity and flexibility of their slim cousins. Arms of the spectators clapped thunder in admiration and solidarity with fellow arms, which upset the legs a great deal. But they were not about to concede: even as they sat

hit; nae ill-willied kerry-on; nae traets or refusin ta tak pairt.

Aims gied oot da first challenge: dey balled a piece a wid apö da grund. Da Leg, da left or richt een, or tagidder, was ta pick up da piece o wid fae da grund an bal hit. Da twa Legs could spaek wi een anidder, at ony time dey wantit, an mak ös o der taes, edder een at a time or tagidder, in ony oarder sae is dey could lift da wid. Dey tried ta turn hit owre; shiv hit; dey tried aa wyes o kinda wirkin tagidder but dey couldna richtly pick hit up: an as fur mövin hit, da ill-best dey could dö wis keek hit twartree inches awa. Seein dis, Fingers tiggit soonds fae da Mooth an gaffed, an gaffed. Airms, da challenger, penkit aboot laek as if hit wis a beauty contest, shaain aff der slim luiks, an dan in a lok o different wyes, liftit up da bit o wid. Dey balled hit far inta da forest. Aaboady takkin pairt or jöst watchin tagidder löt oot a soch, tinkin hit braa. Dey shad aff idder skills an aa: dey liftit mintie grains o saand fae a bowl o rice; dey treedit needles; dey med peerie mootie pulleys fur mövin haevier wid; dey med some spears an balled dem a braa distance; mövs an acts da taes could only draem aboot. Legs could only set dem dere, gaanin, an strangin at da vynd an nyiff wyes o der slim coushins. Fur dem wi airms at wis watchin, dey brocht der airms tagidder lood as thunder, plaesed wi der team speerit, dat wye annoyin da legs a braa coarn. But dey wirna aboot ta gie in; even as dey set dem dere kinda dumpised, der muckle taes drittlin peerie circles i da saand, dey wir tryin ta wirk oot a winnin challenge.

At last, hit wis da turn o legs an taes ta set oot a challenge. Der een, dey

there looking a little bit glum, their big toes drooling little circles on the sand, they were trying to figure out a winning challenge.

At last, it was the turn of legs and toes to issue a challenge. Theirs, they said, was simple. Hands should carry the whole body from one part of the circle to the other. What a stupid challenge, thought the arrogant fingers. It was a sight to see. Everything about the body was upside down. Hands touched the ground; eyes were close to the ground, their angles of vision severely restricted by their proximity to the ground; dust entered the nose, causing it to sneeze; legs and toes floated in the air: nyayo juu, the spectators shouted, and sang playfully.

Nyayo Nyayo juu
Hakuna matata
Fuata Nyayo
Hakuna matata
Turukeni angani

But their attention was fixed on the hands and arms. Organs that only a few minutes before were displaying an incredible array of skills, could hardly move a yard. A few steps, the hands cried out in pain, the arms staggered, wobbled, and let the body fall. They rested and then made another attempt. This time they tried to spread out the fingers the better to hold the ground but only the thumbs were able to stretch. They tried cartwheels but this move was disqualified because for its completion it involved the legs as well. It was the turn of the toes to laugh. They borrowed thick throatal tones from the mouth to contrast their laugh from the squeaky tones the

said, was simple. Haands sud kerry da hale boady fae wan pairt o da circle tae da tidder, Whitna daft test, tocht da fingers, kinda foo o demsels. Hit wis a sicht fur sore een. Aathin aboot da boady wis tapsalteerie. Haands touched da grund; een wis braaly clos tae da grund makkin hit herd ta see richtly; da nose got shockit wi stoor, makkin hit neeze; legs an taes wis aa owre da place: *nyayo juu*, da fock watchin shoutit, an sang wi a kinda skyimp.

Nyayo Nyayo juu
Hakuna matata
Fuata Nyayo
Hakuna matata
Turukeni angani

But dey couldna tak der een affa da haands an airms; organs dat nae time afore wis shaain aff der vynds, a graet haep o dem. Dey could barely möv a yerd. Twartree steps, an da haands wis screchin wi da stangs, da airms swaandered aboot, waavelled, an löt da boady faa tae da grund. Dey salistit, an dan tried again. Dis time dey tried ta spread oot der fingers sae as dey could balance apö da grund a coarn better but only da tooms wis able to rek oot. Dey tried kertwheels but dis möv was banned since, ta dö hit richtly, da legs hed ta play a pairt an aa. Hit wis da turn o da taes ta laach an scoarn. Dey borrowed tick, groff soonds fae da mooth, ta mak a differ wi der laach fae da pleepsit soonds da fingers wis ösed. Hearin da afftaks, da airms wis braally mad an dey hed wan hidmist shot at kerryin da boady. Dey didna manage a single step. Pyaagit, da haands an fingers gae up. Da legs wis blyde ta shaa aff der

fingers had used. Hearing the scorn, the arms were very angry and they made one desperate attempt to carry the body. They did not manage a step. Exhausted the hands and fingers gave up. The legs were happy to display their athletic prowess: they marked time, trotted, ran, made a few high jumps, long jumps, without once letting the body fall. All the feet of the spectators stamped the ground in approval and solidarity. Arms raised their hands to protest this unsportslimbship, conveniently forgetting that they had started the game.

But all of them, including the spectators, noted something strange about the arms: the thumbs which had stretched out when the hands were trying to carry the body, remained separated from the other fingers. The rival organs were about to resume their laughter when they noted something else; far from the separated thumb making the hands less efficient, it enhanced their crasping and grasping power. What's this? Deformity transformed into the power of forming! The debate among the organs to decide the winner went on for five days, the number of fingers and toes on each limb. But try as they could they were not able declare a clear winner; each set of limbs was best at what they did best; none could do without the other. There begun a session of philosophical speculation: what was the body anyway, they all asked, and they realized the body was them all together; they were into each other. Every organ had to function well for all to function well.

But to prevent such a contest in the future and to prevent their getting in each others way, it was decided by all the organs, that thenceforth the body would walk stimna an swack wyes: dey markit time, skelpit on, ran, dey loupit up heich or owre a great lent twartree times, ithoot eence lattin da boady faa. Aa da feet o dem at wis watchin stampit da grund laek as if dey wir brally plaesed. Airms raised der haands ta protest dis unsporty behaviour as if, fur a meenit, dey wir forgyattan dat hit wis dem at wis stertit da game.

But aaboady, even dem jöst watchin, noteeced somethin queer aboot da airms: da tooms dat wis rekkit oot whan da haands wis bön tryin ta kerry da boady, wir stucken apairt fae da tidder fingers. Da rival organs wis laek tae stert gaffin again whan dey noteeced somethin idder; redder as mak da haands o less ös, da separatit toom lat da haand clesp an grab a lok better. My gori! Whit seemed laek deformity wis transformed inta da pooer o creatin! Fur five hael days – da sam number as da fingers an taes apön ivery limb – da organs traepit aboot wha wis won. But try as dey micht dey couldna decide apön a clear winner; ivery set o limbs wis best at whit dey did best; nane could manage ithoot da tidder. Dey began ta tink braally seriously: whit wis da boady onywye, dey aa aksed, an dey realised da boady wis dem aa wirkin tagidder; dey wir pairt o een anidder. Dey aa hed ta wirk weel for da hael caboodle ta wirk weel.

But ta hinder sic a contest i da future an ta hinder dem gyettin in each idder's wye, hit wis decidit bi aa da organs dat, fae noo on, da boady wid walk upricht, feet firmly apö da grund an airms ita da air. Da boady wis blyde aboot da decision but wid alloo peerie bairns ta arl alang ösin airms an legs so as not ta foryet der beginnings.

upright, feet firmly on the ground and arms up in the air. The body was happy with the decision but it would allow children to walk on all fours so as not to forget their origins. They divided tasks: the legs would carry the body but once they got to the destination, hands would do all the work that needed making or holding tools. While the legs and feet did the heavy duty of carrying, the hands reached out and used their skills to work the environment, and ensure that food reached the mouth. Mouth, or rather, its teeth, would chew it, and send it down the throat to the tummy. Tummy would squeeze all the goodness and then pour it into its system of canals through which the goodness would be distributed to all the nooks and crooks of the body. Then tummy would take the used material into its sewage system, from where the body would deposit it in the open fields or bury it under the soil to enrich it. Plants would grow bear fruit; hands would pluck pick some of it and put in the mouth. Oh, yes, the circle of life.

Even games and entertainments were divided accordingly: singing, laughing and talking were left to the mouth; running and soccer largely left to the legs; while baseball and basketball were reserved for the hands, except that the legs were to do the running. In athletics, the legs had all the field to themselves, largely. The clear division of labor made the human body a formidable bio machine, outwitting even the largest of animals in what it could achieve in quantity and quality.

However the organs of the body realized that the permanent arrangement they had arrived at could still bring conflict. The head being up there might

Dey pairtit da jobs: da legs wid kerry da boady but wance dey wan whaar dey wir gyaain, haands wid dö aa da wark dat wis needit, makkin or haddin tools. While da legs an feet bör da back burdeens, da haands rekkit oot an ösed da vynd dey hed ta wirk da laand an mak sure dat fock hed maet i da mooth. Mooth, or redder, da teeth, wid shampse awa at da maet an send hit doon da trot ta da stamack. Stamack wid birze aa da keetchin oot o hit an dan poor hit inta hits system o canals dat wid send hit tae aa da hiddled awa places o da boady. Dan stamack wid pit da ösed gaer inta hits puddins, reed an sparl, fae whaar da boady wid dump hit apö da rigs or böry hit anunder da aert ta mak hit mair fertile. Plants wid growe, bear fruit; haands wid ripe some o hit an pit hit i da mooth. Oh ya, da circle o life.

Even games an sprees wis pairtit da sam wye: singin, gaffin an sheeksin wis left tae da mooth; rinnin an playin fitbaa maistlins left tae da legs; while baa games wis left tae da haands, but dat da legs wis ta dö da rinnin. For rinnin an jimpin, dat wis left tae da legs, near enyoch. Dis clear pairtin o da wark med da human boady a most parteeklar bio-machine, better as even da maist undömious o animals in whit hit could dö, whedder in quantity or quality.

Foosomivver da organs o da human boady cam ta see dat dis final understandin dey wir wirkit oot could still bring argie-bargie. Da head, bein up abön, micht mak hit feel dat hit wis better dan da feet dat touched da grund; or dat hit wis tapster an da organs below hit, jöst servants. Da organs med hit clear dat, in terms o pooer,

make it feel that it was better than the feet that touched the ground or that it was the master and the organs below it, servants only. They stressed that in terms of power, the head and whatever was below it, were equal. To underline this, the organs made sure that pain and joy of any one of the organs was felt by all. They warned the mouth that when saying my this and that, it was talking as the whole body and not as the sole owner.

They sang:

In our body
There's no servant
In our body
There's no servant
We serve one another
Us for Us
We serve one another
Us for Us
We serve one another
The tongue our voice
Hold me and I hold you
We build healthy body
Hold me and I hold you
We build healthy body
Beauty is unity
Together we work
For a healthy body
  Together we work
  For a healthy body
  Unity is our power

This became the All Body Anthem. The body sings is to this day and this is what tells the difference between humans and animals, or those that rejected the upright revolution. Despite what they saw, the four-legged animals would have none of this revolution. The singing

da head an whitivver was below hit, wis wirt da sam. To mak dis plain, da organs med sure dat pain an joy o ony een o da organs wis felt by dem aa. Dey counselled da mooth dat whan sayin *my dis an dat*, hit wis spaekin as da hael boady an no as da only een at aaned hit.

Dey sang:

I wir boady
Der nae servant
I wir boady
Der nae servant
We serve een anidder
Wis fur Wis
We serve een anidder
Wis fur Wis
We serve een anidder
Da tongue wir voice
Hadd me an I hadd you
We bigg a healty boady
Hadd me an I hadd you
We bigg a healty boady
Beauty is bein wan
Tagidder we varg
Fur a healty boady
  Tagidder we varg
  Fur a healty boady
  Wir pooer is in bein wan

Dis cam ta be caaed da Hael Boady Sang. Da boady sings hit even ta dis day an dis whit maks da differ atween humans an animals, dem dat rejectit da 'upricht revolution'. But nivver leetin what dey saa, da fowr-leggit animals wid hae naethin ta dö wi dis revolution. Dis singin onkerry wis jöst a haiverin. Da mooth wis med ta aet an no ta sing. Dey stertit nature's conservative pairty an stack wi der wyes, nivver laek ta change.

business was ridiculous. The mouth was made to eat and not to sing. They formed nature's conservative party and stuck to their ways never changing their habits.

When humans learn from the network of organs, they do well; but when they see the body and the head as parties at war, one being atop of the other, they come close to their animal cousins who rejected the upright revolution.

Whan humans laern fae da clamjamrie o organs, dey dö weel; but whan dey see da boady an da head no as freends but instead, see wan as tapster, dey come clos tae der animal cooshins dat rejectit da upright revolution.

Amanuensis

Marcas Mac an Tuairneir

'S aithne dhomh thu tro fhaclan,
a dh'iarras sgailc is crith a chur
seach miann do chiall,

nach sheas leis fhèin, gun
cheangal-lìn do dh'fhaidhle fuaime,
làn dhìot aig àrd do chlaiginn;
clamhan laigheach na mo chluas.

B' fheàirrde greis uaigneis
a chluinntinn; na smuaintean
diogach a nì sealg a' ghleoc
is tu leat fhèin an uchd do dheasg,

gun fheum air èisteachd.
'S lugha fiù 's, iùnnrais tuineil,
buill-bodhaig is aigeallain-cluais'.

Thoir dhomh na tha nad bhroinn,
seach na chuireadh tu air leth
aig feadhainn eu-choltach riut;
bana-bhaird bhalbh à sealladh.

Sgrìobh sinn fhìn, fada o
bhathar fiosrach ort; mus do
ghrèimich do làmh bhalachail
peann, mus do chaith thu

an dubh-sgrìobhaidh,
do-sgriosta thar an talla làn.
'S mar sin, chan thu an

amanuensis, ach guth a-mhàin,
air leth, nach lugha, a shireas
fhathast a langanaich fhad 's
a sheinnear òran leighis.

Figh, dhòmhsa, faclan a-
steach do thapais fharsaing.
Seachain lainnir shaith nan
snàithlean-òir, a ghoideadh

an soillse a chom-pàirtich
sinn a-riamh, romhad.
Tagh clò buan, na àite.

Ged gun mhaise sin no
ascaoin do bhas na làimh',
ceann ga bhleith is loireach;
dh'fhaoidte gum mair e an aois.

Radials

Maria Sledmere

He sleeps so he cannot be woken.
Why does it hurt to see a sky this blue?
There are rivers you could not possibly cross
without some kind of sentence. I suppose
it is a question of one's feline nature.
We lay in the dark discussing astrology
by which I mean the quivering of two stars meeting
at the point of a tangent.
The water runs hot when you touch it, cools when you are not
quite here but listening. I know you are
because there was this thing you wrote in your phone
I've since forgotten. I remember us soft and milky,
licking the air like fur. So many people
no longer purchase records. There is this dust
that tastes of ashes, gravel, every cigarette
smoked on a Lou Reed dawn. By which I mean
the closeness of sofas and photographs
mincing our intimacy in the company of others.
There is always this talk and this circling
backwards to the end, the needle, the blue.
I'm sorry that deep down we both understand
and I wish I could sleep like you:
sleep as if time was something you fell through
sleep as if there was someone to cling to.

Essay in Firs

Maria Sledmere

This is a night
and I guess it's only a night
if someone's buying you drinks.

I try to look auburn,
radiant; something like how
a tree must feel
when its age dissolves into youth.

How long does a tree live?
I've lived a very long time
or not long at all
by standards of flesh. I love
lush things
like sugar loves milk.

There is blue sometimes
just powdering outwards.

If the darkness cuts you down
there's always a pool of neon,
clink of glass and bone.

Whatever you say
you can say it again
at 3am for effect.

It's in this sense alone
that I love you.

Five Poems about Men and War

Mark Russell

MEN HIDING IN THE TOMBS OF THEIR FATHERS

About war, they say, there is nothing new to confuse us. It is as common to scour the undergrowth for kindling, as it is to boil snow and grass for soup. It is the nightly airstrike, and by equal turns, the daytime shelling, that may explain the absence of a subplot. A man whose face is pressed to the window of the bus may be leaving his country forever, or finding water where he can. Two men whose faces are pressed to the window of the bus may have just resumed their friendship after thirty years of hostilities, or going on a summer holiday.

MEN WHO BELIEVE THEY ARE THEODORE ROOSEVELT

About war, they say, there is nothing new to silence us. It is as common to plan a series of five novels on the conquest of native peoples by white Europeans, as it is to complete only three and be murdered on the cathedral steps. It is the tension between tradition and modernity, and by equal turns, the cross-fertilisation of two cultures, that may have us scrabbling in the mud for the nuclear codes. A man who travels across continents to shoot a bear may be settling an old score, or have complicated relationships with women not solved by the assurance that size doesn't matter. Two men who travel across continents

to shoot a bear may be members of the
Boone and Crockett Club advocating the
principles of the fair chase, or have
complicated relationships with men not
solved by the assurance that size doesn't matter.

MEN WITH HEADS FOR MATHEMATICS

About war, they say, there is nothing new to
Bcc the members of your email contact group.
It is as common to focus on the evidence
provided by the Food and Drugs
Administration, as it is to allow a special agent
to languish in an alien penal colony. It is the
slaying of your mother's son, and by equal
turns, the marriage to your mother's sister,
that may establish you in the eyes of the
populace (excluding your mother, whom you
can lock up in a tower) as a man who can
get things done. A man who sees war as the
logical extension of foreign policy may own
shares in the Lockheed Martin/Boeing F-22
Raptor, or be an academic associated with the
Stockholm International Peace Research
Institute whose statements are deliberately
decontextualised by Fox News. Two men who
see war as the logical extension of foreign
policy may invoke clichéd Protestant rhetoric
when faced by bereaved mothers, or be open
to persuasion if a trip to Disneyland is mentioned.

MEN PERPLEXED

About war, they say, there is nothing new
about which to be stubborn. It is as common
to be called to the bar after the Restoration,
as it is to watch your parents perish in a
great fire. It is the machinations within the
court during the dying days of a childless

monarch, and by equal turns, the advice of partial councillors, that may lead the nobles to invite invasion by the King of Somewhere Else. A man found ſtabbed in his bed may have been controversially appointed to the Queen's Privy Chamber, or have juſt announced his intention to run for nomination as the Republican Party's Presidential candidate. Two men found ſtabbed in their beds may have been messengers from the Danish court, or printers of Renaissance folios unwilling to accept that there may be more than three dramatic genres.

MEN USING PSEUDONYMS

About war, they say, there is nothing new to soliloquise. It is as common to witness the decline of a once-noble hero, as it is to eat pies made of tiny tots. It is the heavy soil under which the false accusers lie, and by equal turns, the extravagant pyres on which the falsely accused burn, that may turn grief into vengeance. A man told he muſt die in order that morality be reſtored to the social world may agree with the notion that the greater good requires juſt such a sacrifice, or claim to be an atheiſt. Two men told they muſt die in order that morality be reſtored to the social world may queſtion the lateſt interpretations of moral law, or suggeſt the identities of alternative gentlemen who could pay the ultimate price, and who can be found in plentiful number among the slums and barrios of all our cities.

Punkt

Lucy Cathcart Froden

)

You, the held
Clumsy stowaway
I, the hold

;

I, the listing
Vasa, top heavy
Corn sheaf fool

—

Molten, poured
Foundry-flat I am
Spread your map

:

Insides out
A raw symmetry
Kneel, hide, lie

¶

You the mast
That will punctuate
This vessel

A Modern Love Poem

Iona Lee

Honey, I would suffer Scotrail for you.
I'd pay the £12.60 from Glasgow to Edinburgh
just to see you for one stolen evening.
I know its no driving through the night
with a rain soaked window
but I can't afford a car.

Sweetheart, I would thole that annoying friend of
yours,
the one who always calls me 'Dude',
and eats with his mouth open.

Darling, I would go on the pill for you.
I'd let my boobs swell to twice their normal size,
which I know that you don't really mind.
I would weather the mood swings
and feeling like I'm lying on a sheet of glass,
my emotions a river beneath.

Babe, I'd meet your parents if you wanted.
I'd compliment Lynn on her lasagne
and watch snooker with Brian
and I wouldn't even mention
that I'd been at a gay bar the night before.

My love, I would consider trying anal for you.
I know that you're not really interested either,
but, if you were, and you gave me a few days notice,
I would definitely keep it in mind.

I would share my Netflix password with you.
I would listen to Captain Beefheart or Frank Zappa
for you.
I would stroke your hair while you were in a K-hole.

Oh my love, let's get lost in a giant Tesco together.
Let's half an avocado.

I want to not be able to afford travelling with you
and go Facebook official.
I want to do Buzzfeed quizzes
and smoke dodgy weed.
and I want you to be the one
who calms me from my panic attack
after.

Let's make love!
Quietly, so your flatmate doesn't hear.
After all, aren't orgasms just really fun panic attacks?

Three Young Women on the Train: In Conversation

Olive M Ritch

I

me me me me me me me me me me me me me me
me me me me me me me me me me me me me me
me me me me me me me me me me me me me me
me me me me me me me me me me me me me me
me me me me me me me me me me me me me me
me me me me me me me me me me me me me me
me me me me me me me me me me me me me me
me me me me me me me me me me me me me me
me me me me me me me me me me me me me me
me me me me me me me me me me me me me me
me me me me me me me me me me me me me me
me me me me me me me me me me me me me me
me me me me me me me me me me me me me me
me me me me me me me me me me me me me me

II

me me me me me me me me me me me me me me me
me me me me me me me me me me me me me me me
me me me me me me me me me me me me me me me
me me me me me me me me me me me me me me me
me me me me me me me me me me me me me me me
me me me me me me me me me me me me me me me
me me me me me me me me me me me me me me me
me me me me me me me me me me me me me me me
me me me me me me me me me me me me me me me
me me me me me me me me me me me me me me me
me me me me me me me me me me me me me me me
me me me me me me me me me me me me me me me
me me me me me me me me me me me me me me me
me me me me me me me me me me me me me me me

III

me me me me me me me me me me me me me me
me me me me me me me me me me me me me me
me me me me me me me me me me me me me me
me me me me me me me me me me me me me me
me me me me me me me me me me me me me me
me me me me me me me me me me me me me me
me me me me me me me me me me me me me me
me me me me me me me me me me me me me me
me me me me me me me me me me me me me me
me me me me me me me me me me me me me me
me me me me me me me me me me me me me me
me me me me me me me me me me me me me me
me me me me me me me me me me me me me me
me me me me me me me me me me me me me me

45 Minutes Uphill to Waverley

Rosa Campbell

yellowish clouds hang like cigarette smoke
above Leith Walk as an Algerian man joins the surge
crossing the road to an early dinner, feeling
behind him for his wife's hand, an anchor
in the 6pm crush
                              battling the other way
someone dark-haired and elegant holds three bottles
of Diet Coke between the fingers of one hand, &
enters the stage door of the Playhouse – smug
with what separates them from us
                                        I suppose
you never lose that. An Italian greyhound &
one of those dogs that looks like fried chicken
appear by the kerb & I cannot meet their eyes
otherwise I will stay forever and miss my train
but I allow myself the luxury of a glance
at my own reflection:
                              four teenage boys
sit at a round table in a curry house, all elbows
& their empty plates are so vulnerable it almost
knocks the wind right out of me, their hands
lying by the knives as if they are playing at knights
but have forgotten their costumes
                                        a waitress
is tucked into the corner of the frame & whistles
an approximation of Ode to Joy between drags
& when my mouth twitches she winks
                                        the light
is spongy gold & it is late September & everything
blushes as we stream together into evening

Poem

Hannah Van Hove

I was sitting in the windowless meeting room.

I was eating cake at the café round the corner.

I was wondering about things like stability.

I was at a poetry reading in a tiny gallery.

I was thinking about the relation of form to content, content to form.

I thought how difficult it seemed to get anything done.

I was lying in the bath at my parents' house.

I was thinking about my dog who had growled at me.

I was angry at the person who had smiled at me.

I was lying on the couch at my friend's place.

I was thinking about turning 30 and wondering if I was depressed about it.

I was cooking dinner in a bright kitchen.

I was thinking everything would probably always be difficult and tiring to do.

I was lighting the fire in a cottage up north.

I was driving a hired van.

I was hurrying home from work.

I was so happy and content I thought I could easily break.

I was getting the bus to work.

I was sobbing in the church.

I was thinking about impermanence and light and radiance.

I was shopping in the supermarket.

I was heaving furniture up the stairs.

I was reading on the beach in the sun.

I was sheltered and brimming with love.

I was watering plants in our flat.

I was playing with my friend's three-year old.

I was buying flowers after work.

I was thinking how little thinking I seem to do.

I was wondering about mundanity, inanity, myself.

I was waitressing in a busy restaurant.

I was looking up books in a library.

I was tired and aching and grumpy.

I was pretending to sleep on the train.

I was drinking wine and feeling sick.

I was riding a bike in a foreign city.

I was trying to remember my first day at school.

I was collecting leaves with my sisters.

Mischief

Peter McCune

A little lick of wallpaper had come unstuck at the seam and he knew he had to tug at it to find out how much more of the paper had lost its stickiness. It was impossible to know how long it had been there, jutting out of the wall, a little flap of imperfection begging to be pulled. Maggie would've said it wasn't that bad, or rubbed a bit of Pritt Stick on it and pushed it back down.

It was hotter than usual for May, and it was probably this heat and the humidity that had caused the paper to come away from the wall. It was a mercy that the kitchen was the only room in the house with wallpaper or he'd be plagued with little tags of paper everywhere he went.

He knew he probably shouldn't pull it. But he also knew he would pull it eventually, so the sooner he did it the sooner he could stop thinking about it.

He gripped the lip of wallpaper with his thumb and forefinger and realised that he hadn't even decided what to do with the little fucker – whether he was going to rip it off without causing any more damage or get right under it and find out the extent of the thing.

Fuck it.

He pulled softly and the paper peeled away from the wall like sweaty plastic cheese off a burger. Good thing he hadn't eaten much in a while or the thought might've turned him. As the strip of paper grew in his right hand, he used his left to guide it along, keeping it in one satisfying piece, like peeling the perfect orange. It was coming away nicely and he'd kept it pretty much intact when part of the paper stuck fast to the wall and the piece in his hands tore away from the rest and hung lank and heavy in his hands. He studied it for a moment. He sniffed it and found that he recognised the fishy smell of the recently rehydrated wallpaper paste. You wouldn't think the smell of paste would stick in your mind for all you're exposed to it, and Maggie had done most of the painting and decorating, so maybe he'd never actually smelled this paste before. Maybe this smell was like something else he's experienced and he's just forgotten what it was? Perhaps Maggie had some product that smelled like paste – some fancy make-up or moisturiser?

Anyway, there wasn't time to get into that; there was another good-looking flap of wallpaper on the opposite side of the seam just asking for it. But when he pulled, it ripped off into a little misshapen stamp.

Fuck!

That was no good at all. He'd get the kettle on and see if a splash of boiling water would loosen it. Of course it would. He'd have to take the whole lot off as soon as possible. It'd take the rest of the day, at least. It was a shitty job, but no one else was going to do it.

The following week, he found a little loop of maroon wool pulled out of his favourite jumper. He didn't normally wear jumpers inside his house in the middle of summer but he'd been forced to smash out two of the windows in the living room on Sunday when he found a little fracture snaking its way up the glass. These things start with small fractures and then the whole mess is coming down and there's nothing you can do to stop it. Better to just smash it yourself, on your own terms.

The loop of wool came away easily enough once he managed to force his finger through and get a good grip. Then it was just a matter of pulling and pulling until the wool was completely untangled.

That's all jumpers are, anyway: tangled-up wool. He'd stick to waxed jackets from now on and those waterproof coats made from plastic.

The maroon wool poured out across the floor in front of him and there was so much more of it now that it was just wool and not a jumper. It had trebled in size and when he got down on his belly and buried his head in the pile it looked like dried-up intestines. Maggie had loved this jumper. Had she bought it for him? It was too long ago to remember now.

Pulling the carpet up in the bedroom was a tough job without the right tools – and a claw hammer and rusty chisel were not the right tools. But he'd found two beetles and an earwig tickling along in the thick magnolia shag and he wasn't just going to sit around and let the infestation go full swing.

To rip all the carpet up, he had to move the dressing table into the landing. Then the bed, then the chest of drawers and anything else too big to just topple and send flying when he yanked the carpet up hard, sending dust everywhere. The dust coated his teeth and settled into his pores and he wondered if dust was just dead skin cells then some of it might've been Maggie – tiny little parts of her hiding in the carpet.

When he lifted one of the bedside tables, the drawer slid open and he found an old letter in his handwriting that he must've written years ago. He didn't know where to sit, so he pushed some of the carpet to the edges of the room, where it bulged like flabby folds of skin, then he sat down on the bare floorboards to read the letter.

The letter was only a few pages long, but he studied it so closely that it was almost dark by the time he'd finished reading. He hadn't thought to turn on the light until he realised he was straining to read the last few sentences. He got up, turned on the light, and looked for a red pen to start editing. There were all kinds of problems with the grammar, punctuation, spelling, lies, lost vocabulary, emotions he couldn't remember feeling and some he remembered too well. He began by scoring out the words '~~your perfume~~'. He liked the look of it better this way, but then the next part didn't make sense, so he scored out '~~intoxicating~~'. Then he scored out '~~I miss your cackling, witch's laugh when I do something stupid or stump my toe on the coffee table~~'. But with that sentence gone most of that page didn't feel right anymore and he had to put a red line through every word. Then, because he'd scored out 'miss' a few times on that page, he had to be consistent and get rid of the rest. He managed to find eleven instances of 'miss' and he put a red line through each one. This was a tough letter to edit and he hadn't even begun to score out the promises he'd made.

Finally, he was just left with one word right at the start. *Dear*. It didn't make sense to him. Had that word ever made sense? He'd come this far, so he might as well finish it.

He was so busy he didn't have time to go out and ask anyone else if their homes were falling apart too. Had they even noticed how bad it had got? He couldn't even ask a guest because no one had visited in months – and he would've known if they'd visited in the last few days because he would've heard them through the empty windowpanes and seen them through the doorless doorframe.

By then, he was forced to spend most of his time fixing the little problems. He took the legs off the chairs because the wobbling might've caused an accident and he was forced to unscrew the rest of the doors from their hinges to stop them from creaking and eventually snapping off all on their own. He had to take all the fraying covers off Maggie's books, then rip out the folded and dog-eared pages, then unravel her clothes and his clothes and tear off the door handles and his fingernails and the rooftiles and the scraggy skin around his lips. But it was probably good to keep busy. At least it kept him out of his head and out of mischief.

From Riddles

Vahni Capildeo

I.
Chairs. Ruthless cornfield.
Counters. Writless canefield.
Lotus. Lotusless CCTV.
Children. Fingers. Children.
Voices. Children. Dodges.
Self-rearranging furniture.
Polytheist plastic. Christmas.
Treble-clef rug.

II.
Landscape: aeroplanes::
helplessness: fertilizer.
Fear. Change.
What is as beautiful:
local birdwatchers,
in a zone reported
globally for tinpots,
wind, wars.

III.
Fastidious taste.
Calligraphy or graffiti
only. Novels
dead and at length
only. So,
so quick, unprompted
birdsong laughter.
So, so quiet
a step ahead.
Espresso on gelato.
Only contempt
the cold with the turkey.
Only contempt
the trap with the honey.

Envoi

Vahni Capildeo

[...] each your doing,
So singular in each particular,
Crowns what you are doing in the present deed,
That all your acts are queens.
Shakespeare, The Winter's Tale IV. iv.

green green
blue green
tray of arrows
tray of stars
my enteared heart
my enearthed heart
what would you
do you know

The Many Voices Project

Scottish PEN

Many Voices is an ongoing project by Scottish PEN which aims to amplify those silenced, marginalised, or disproportionally absent from written expression or public conversation. The first round, from which the following individual and collaborative pieces are a sample, saw writers work with six groups across Scotland on workshops and events: Apex Scotland, HMYOI Polmont, International Women's Group Glasgow, LGBT Youth Scotland, Move On and Orkney Library & Archive. Not only can access to writing support be an important tool for personal expression, but it can broaden understandings of the world we live in today and the stories we tell about it.

Moving

Anonymous

after Marjorie Lotfi Gill

She wanted to leave a light on
a small garden full of jasmine and roses,
a lemon tree for summer,
fresh mint in a pot and sunflowers indoors.
She wanted to leave a card with words,
and *caravan* bread and salt, milk
and sugar for welcome, a blue eye,
a bronze hand and a horseshoe
for safety, for luck.

Untitled

Anonymous

Not all heroes wear capes
my hero wore a purple anorak
Not all heroes are physically strong
My hero was five foot tall
Not all heroes can fly
My hero drove a Ford Fiesta
Not all heroes save the world
My hero saved me
Not all heroes wear capes

Gossip Broth

Caroline Hume

Tak twa cleckin hens
Add a dod o Sheriff Coort
And 'fur whit a neep'
A navefu o Radio Orkney
Moan, girn and pleep
Simmer gently

Turn up the haet wae "whaur's
hivvin an affair"
Water liberally wae supposition
Gae hid a good steer
Spice hid up, pepper wae exaggeration
Bring to a rolling boil

Haev in a puckle o drukken carry-ons
And a mense o indignation
A liv o 'Ye'll nivver guess whit ah've heard'
And a muckle drap o pooshan
Simmer for an oor or twa

Than share equally amang freends

Untitled

Ingrid Grieve

The dowdoswang roars
I stand on the shore, chist me
Exhilarated

A great golder fae West
Oot in the green blue haaf
The whaalbacks dance

A whummelan sky
Meets a dark ill trickit sea
The raingoose sings

The sky cam doon
And danced wae the trimsan sea
No fisheen the day

A Coorsh Day

Ingrid Grieve

· 'Whit a Helziegaitha!'
'Aye…it's a bit Airy'
'Airy! It's Howalee!
The sky's Hammermuggley
and the sea's Choldertow
and Kellyan Hellyan!'
· 'Ahh bit it's Gyran noo
startan tae Quoy
afore long it'll be Orquil'

Out of Sight

Anonymous

She packs the smallest cup – the last piece
of her mother's collection – into the suitcase,
because she only likes exactly this much
black coffee mornings, sugared with Sweetex.

She adds the box of sea glass –
grass green, cloud white, soil brown
sea and sapphire blue – from different
seas in different countries.

She can't choose between her two
wooden hearts. To her, they look like
love – strong and light, too hard
to break, soft to the touch, with a ring
for every year – so she slips one
in her pocket and the other
in the case for the people she loves.

She adds a blank notebook
so she can write down her history.

She closes her door and keeps the key
to remind her of home, imagines it becomes
a key to her future, will open every door,
every heart, every case she will carry.

She takes small images to protect her,
help her to pray, and her small Koran or bible, that fits
neatly into the palm of her hand.

She chooses her grandmother's brightest scarves –
blue and white and red and yellow, spotted and striped
and starred – to cover her head for church or mosque,
to go out amongst strangers, or just for remembering.

She wants to bring her great grandmother's heirloom,
hidden in an ordinary box under old clothes
in the cellar: the handmade fragile egg, rimmed with gold
and silver, diamonds. She wraps it in the scarves,
hopes someday to set it out for others to see.

She throws a toy train in the suitcase
for her children or children's children,
or the children she'll be visiting,
adds a map of the place she is headed,
so she will always know where she is.

She brings her crochet needles for lace –
half way through the project –
so she has something to keep her hands busy.

At the last minute she adds tiny binoculars,
to see nature around her on the journey,
to be able to see what is just out of sight.

Untitled

Caroline Hume

Da on the tractor
Granny sat on the binder
Daein the hard wark

Untitled

Barbara Johnston

cattieface swoopan
eyes locked on the grund below
peedie vole tremblan.

scorrie on the gress
yillow feet gaan up an doon
lukkan fur a wurm.

sun warm on me face
hid's a day atween weathers
bitter wind the nixt.

Going Home

Anonymous

Fresh sardines straight from the sea
The smell of winter – frozen weather, Christmas trees, clementines
Visiting my mother's grave
The company of a warm family at every event, family parties
No longer worries about being misunderstood
Visiting my brother at the cemetery every Friday, bringing flowers
Feeding my cat
Being with people who remember your life
Getting caught out on my bad language
The right sabzi ras el hanout, bardagoush, mint, saffron and olive oil
To be with my son and sister and brother in Libya
Drinking small cups of coffee on the roof
Catching up with childhood friends on motherhood, how time has passed
Mama's couscous every Friday – meat potatoes, red vegetable sauce
Beautiful kaftan and kabilijobha and karako and shidha and erhda
Dancing at my brother's wedding

Black and White and Read All Over

Animal Lovers
Rob Palk

Sandstone, RRP £8.99, 304pp

As a genre, the rom-com is an evolutionary dead end. Not Romance, mind you. As long as there's love, there'll be Romance, of which the rom-com is merely a mutation. But its fluffy will-they-won't-they frisson often hides a toxic bite: one person bulldozing the other's preferences until they just, well, *give in* to love. As the politics of emotional autonomy progress, what was cute up close becomes grotesque from far away – and it makes for an uncomfortable start to Rob Palk's *Animal Lovers*.

Marie, Stuart's wife of four months, has left him to go protest badger culls in Gloucester. In response, he fakes an interest in the cause, to get near to her, to convince her to abandon her new interest, to win her back from a dashing rival. It's a classic rom-com set-up, which in 2018 feels archaic and a bit creepy. Doesn't Marie know her own mind, or can't Stuart at least let her own her decisions? Despite Stuart's sympathetic backstory – an early stroke, partially sighted, a niggling class-consciousness – from the outset you sort of hope he fails.

Then again, in *Animal Lovers*, the elevator pitch seems wholly unprepared for the complex characters trapped within it. Palk's cast are humans at their most dynamic, clever, caring, snobbish and idiosyncratic. Even the most peripheral characters leave a muddying mark: a brain surgeon bragging about a fame that isn't his; a farmer who sobs over having to butcher his beloved cows, even while he hunts down badgers. These are not simple caricatures. The exception to this is Marie, who in Stuart's telling comes across as a pretty prize for perseverance, and it's possible he doesn't actually have any real clue what he's trying to win back.

There are heavy similarities between Palk and Stuart (*Animal Lovers* was written in the aftermath of Palk's own serious illness and a dissolved marriage), but you get the impression Stuart is less a stand-in for Palk and more of a fall-guy. Sensible, stable characters stand well clear of the mess Stuart gets into, and you get the feeling Palk stands with them, lobbing rotten fruit at a more oblivious version of himself. The only forces pushing Stuart and Marie together, Palk draws in various shades of ridiculous, yet it's these same characters who provide direct entry to the book's themes of toxic masculinity, entitlement and the grey areas where people are animals first, humans second. But Stuart takes so long to wise up, by the time the story reveals itself as more than a basic win-her-back affair, it's almost too late.

Lucky, then, Palk's a witty writer, with an almost Pratchett-esque flair for whimsical turns of phrase that work as their own punchline, deployed best in acerbic character descriptions. Unwashed slacker George has a voice "like two balloons rubbed together" while Marie's renowned hyper-cultured parents are so full of reptilian glamour, her mother's legs have a Spitting Image doll all their own.

It's a shame Palk often betrays his jokes with repetition, explaining them in plainer terms as if worried readers might be left behind, but the frequently nimble dialogue keeps the pace quick, and the characters engaging.

Animal Lovers is a bramble thicket, a real wood with all its barbs and shadows, hidden inside the pruned and trimmed idea of one. It's tempting to rush in and out the other side, but the effort would be exhausting, and you'd miss all the fun. Better instead to take your time with it– and let the wild things reveal themselves in the dark.

– Dangerous Beans

Form and Contentment

Past Love in the Museum of Transport
Ciara MacLaverty

Tapsalteerie, RRP £5.00, 32pp

Ciara MacLaverty's first pamphlet, published by Aberdeenshire small press Tapsalteerie, is a thing of subtle beauty. The overarching mood of its twenty-three poems is well-served by its gorgeous cover, which renders Zaha Hadid's eponymous ultramodern building in shades reminiscent of a vintage railway travel poster. It's a stylistic superimposition which captures the poems' layering of past and present. But

while the 'Past Love' of the title might imply longing, these are rather poems of fond nostalgia and quiet optimism, refracted through the simple pleasures of family and community, which is to say (and as the title suggests), love. As the final stanza of the last poem 'Milking Years' puts it:

Forgive me for falling back here.
I'm a grown woman,
more content than I ever expected to be.
It's just the siphoning of a glad heart,
milking years of luck upon luck,
never wanting to spill a drop.

Like the speaker (of whom one gets a strong autobiographical sense), these poems are "content" – with their subjects, their form, their voice, their pace – each the "siphoning of a glad heart". It's a contentment the reader is invited to share in, and indeed its sensitivity – calming, loving, poignant – is often deeply affecting, like the charm of a faded inscription on the inside cover of a second-hand book.

That's not to say the poems are without their tensions and sadnesses, as in 'Don't Touch Jim's Globe', which closes on an ominous note: "Jim's globe lay unspun and dusted on the window sill / while bulldozers waited at the bottom of the hill." But it's characteristic of MacLaverty to resolve these tensions, ultimately celebrating their significance as part of "never wanting to spill a drop". Take "We Were Sailing", for example, where the possibility of catastrophe in opening lines' "I can't believe they let us out there: / two girls in a sailboat" is foreclosed with "life jackets", ultimately concluding with an uplifting "amazement at ourselves". These poems of memory, most prominent in the first half of the sequence, find their complement in poems about the speaker's children in the second half, whereby the coming-of-age in 'Atomic' prefigures the son's excitement in 'The Girl My Boy Loves Walks Past'. It's this sense of family past, present and future which is the pamphlet's 'love', and with it comes a life-affirming sense of continuity, as well as a remarkable consistency of voice.

Only in a couple of poems does MacLaverty apparently stray from this familial, autobiographical thread, most notably in 'This Is Carp', where the 'you' of the poem is neither lover nor relative but the poet herself, making a poem from a frustrated typo. It's telling that the final simile, comparing an "American granny [...] cradling" a carp to "her first child", returns to the poet's preoccupation with family and children; likewise the closing lines of "The Thornwood Sisters", which laments that "[i]n any other life" a local spinster "could have been / someone's mother." We could ask if Ms Thornwood would have wanted to be "someone's mother", which would hint that this familial love gives the pamphlet its limits, as well as its vitality. But as a reader I'm inclined to moot that question, "never wanting", like MacLaverty, "to spill a drop."

– Calum Rodger

Better than nothing but not enough

The Bi-Plane & Other Poems
D M Black

Mariscat Press, RRP £6.00, 32pp

This is another in what has been an excellent series of recent pamphlets from Mariscat Press including those by Evelyn Pye and Jackie Kay. In *The Bi-Plane & Other Poems* there is much to engage with from a writer who has clarity, craft and wisdom. The poems tend towards the psychoanalytic and have something of the flavour of The Frankfurt School about them but without the fundamentally revolutionary foundations of that original movement of intellectuals.

The poems 'Leaving the submarine' (first published in *Gutter 16*) and 'Prévert: *When someone alive kills himself*' are fine studies of alienation and power. In the former a disembodied voice orders men from the world of a submarine out into the 'real' world of a village, where "you will feel critical / of the civilians you encounter" due to the dissolution of predetermined regulations, shock of the new and the random possibilities of new freedoms; vaguely reminiscent of the 1960s TV series 'The Prisoner', 'Prévert...' is probably an allusion to 20th century French poet and theatre activist Jacques Prévert. It is a fine poem on suicide and ideas related thereto:

— And why would he do it?...

And all set about finding responses.

Peculiar and lifeless question, peculiar and lifeless responses.

It also contains the superb line: 'Sometimes a being who adores life kills himself still fully alive and smiles at life as he dies.' This is perhaps an unrealistically romantic notion, but nonetheless recognition of a terrible bravery rather than the common and casual dismissal of suicide as an act of cowardice.

There are also excellent poems on memory and ageing, including the title poem and 'A Stupid Thought.' There are green concerns in 'Thoughts in the presence of trees' and questioning of global trade relations in 'A Shirt from John Lewis'.

These are intellectual poems, well written, well executed and pleasurable to read. Many folk will find something here to enjoy – to bring a knowing wry smile to one's face – but what won't be found is visceral fire: heart, lung and body are subordinated to clarity, technique and prosaic rational abstraction that is insufficient for the critique of contemporary globalism that is being attempted. As such, there is lot of small 'p' politics within the poetry. And because of this it is in danger of becoming akin to the charity worker or the missionary: they might save you from starvation but do not give the means to feed yourself. Another analogy might be that of giving Scotland devolution in order to kill independence. It's better than nothing but, arguably, it isn't enough. The poetic technique is

itself an illustration of class relations and the content reflects the privilege of an education that for many would be very hard won, or utterly inaccessible. Having said this, the twenty poems contained here do make a valuable critique of many aspects of life and the contemporary world, but for this reviewer at least, their ultimate reliance on the spiritual and unknowable detracts from rather than enhances the moral and practical validity of the criticisms.

– Jim Ferguson

For the outcasts

Goblin
Ever Dundas

Saraband, RRP £8.99, 280pp

Goblin has had quite the journey. After a rocky introduction to the world and a difficult adolescence, the novel was rescued from dire straits by Saraband last year, and went on to win the Saltire Society First Book of the Year Award for 2017. For a novel about self-actualisation, identity and rebirth, it couldn't be more perfect.

When we first meet Goblin, she is an 81-year-old reader-in-residence at an Edinburgh library, with a homeless best friend who is eating his way through *Ulysses*–and, in fact, through the building's entire collection. The discovery of "bones, doll parts, a shrew head, a camera" in London around the time of the 2011 riots throws Goblin back into a past that she's done her best to forget through fiction, and the book then flits back and forth, telling us Goblin's life story from 1939 onwards.

Starting with Goblin's discovery of thousands of pets that have been put down at the outbreak of World War II, and spanning the years of the war and the decades afterwards, Dundas takes us through a life of otherness, alienation, acceptance and inclusivity. Goblin, hated by her mother, is evacuated to the country and finds herself in the care of an abusive religious couple. She escapes, and makes her way back to London in the company of Corporal Pig, her brilliantly-named porcine sidekick. In the capital, she lives alone, adopting abandoned animals during the Blitz, creating tales and characters to earn money and support her growing trans-species family. She joins the circus, in passages that owe a lot to Katherine Dunn's *Geek Love* as well as Tod Browning's *Freaks*, and finds herself imprisoned in Poland, in love in Italy, and seeking solace in stories in Scotland.

If this all sounds incredibly quirky—well, it is. The book is very aware of itself, and by dint of this, also forces the reader to be aware of it as an entity, making it difficult to lose yourself in the story. If Goblin herself—hated for being ugly, gendered as both boy and girl, pansexual and unafraid of physical difference—is a symbol of the beauty of freakishness and of a better world in which individuals, human and otherwise, are all considered equal and equally perfect, then the novel takes this symbolism and draws it out to extremes. Goblin's world has little of the nuance of the real world, and perhaps is a better, more pure place for it.

What some readers may see as an overly simplistic moral universe, in which characters are either borderline evil or literally angelic with little motivation to be anything but what they are, others will read as a welcoming and inclusive half-fantasy realm, where strangeness is celebrated and darkness can be escaped or avoided. Of course, Goblin's story is not that simple, and the success of the novel is making the line between the protagonist's real world and her fictionalised history both unclear and vulnerable. Unreliable narrators are always the most interesting, and whether or not you choose to take Goblin at her word, it's difficult not to see her as a fragile creature despite all her self-confidence and boorishness.

This, then, is what elevates the novel from being an escapist fantasy: the acknowledgment that, despite all our best efforts to paint our lives in bright colours, there is an inescapable blackness that at some point must be confronted. Whether or not this novel actually confronts that reality is another question altogether.

– *Minimus*

These Poems Aren't Torpid

Urn & Drum
Lila Matsumoto

Shearsman (2018), RRP £9.95, 72pp

Reading *Urn & Drum*, Lila Matsumoto's first full collection, it occurred to me that rarely has the term 'collection' been better suited to a poetry book. Collection: a 'gathering together'; 'a group of things collected and arranged'. This is what all poetry collections do, I suppose, but Matsumoto's various emphases on objects – most prominently those of the museum and the home – make this convention of naming all the more felicitous. Moreover, the volume is arranged as five discrete sequences, each of which presents a kind of mini-collection within the whole. Two of these – 'Allegories from my Kitchen' and 'Soft Troika' – have been previously published as pamphlets (by Sad Press and If A Leaf Falls Press respectively), and while I perhaps still prefer these poems in their small press forms, they are in fine company in the present gathering: a group of things comprising groups of things.

But what of these things? The first sequence, 'happy work', reproduces images of objects from the Wellcome Library alongside a series of ekphrastic poems. Here, it's not so much that the poems bring the objects to life, but rather reveal the life that's already inside them, as in 'ivory diagnostic figure, reclining':

I often have the feeling I am in bed
rather than being an object
Monday to Friday, I escape the
narrowness and permanence
of definition
The world which surrounds me
is   constantly   catalyzed   by
personalities
whose lives are driven forward
by the spirit of automation
You can see that there is something
alive
or operating
in me

It's not clear here whether the voice is the figure's or the viewer of figure's, and nor should it be. This isn't ventriloquism, but sympathy – a sense of common feeling. What is true of the objects of the museum is also true of the objects of the home, as in 'Fondant Cake':

This fondant cake is here for you. A crisp, almost brittle crust, and a rich dark crumb. Also this grief bacon.

"[G]rief bacon"! A breakfast table loaded with sympathy. However they fix upon or wander from their objects (wandering furthest in the third sequence, 'Landish'), these poems are "constantly catalyzed by personalities", voicing the minute vicissitudes of shared existence in all their timbres and resonances. As such, these poems arrange but, like any good *Wunderkammer*, do not impose order. There's always something tentative about Matsumoto's lines, and tactile. As she writes in the final sequence of poems "Soft Troika", "Objects aren't torpid", and this 'gathering together' is also a feeling through, an experimental circumlocution that grazes in, with and against its objects and their catalysts. To quote another piece from that sequence, it is a 'gently discombobulating' experience – which is to say a pleasurably uncanny one – and when she writes later in that same piece "some days your motility seems to me a strange thing", it may well be the collection itself which she (as 'you', the reader) is addressing. These poems don't fixate on objects, but inhabit them, and in so doing show us, as Matsumoto puts it in 'Morning', that "Life is a kind of theatre where the characters sing or dance most or all of the time." It is a very fine theatre indeed.

– *Calum Rodger*

Ripe & Raw

Mayhem & Death
Helen McClory

404 Ink, RRP £8.99, 208pp

Mayhem & Death is a reminder that we are ultimately at the mercy of the elements and anthropogenic ruin, the extremities of which may rip us out of the reality we've grown used to. Published simultaneously with a new edition of Saltire-winning *On the Edges of Vision*, this second collection of stories ending with a novella is a darker

and stormier night in comparison, as characters grapple with the potential of nature to turn hostile.

In fable-like 'Distinctive Natural Patterns', visiting strangers meet an untimely death when they take soup and shelter. Before death in their sleep and a sky burial, their passage through the landscape is suffused with foreboding.

> "Navigation with foreknowledge of the landscape, alacrity to the interlock of burns and fording points, scramble points, footholds, points above the fog, how long it will take to walk between each with a hand stretched out and the wolves behind you."

'The Beautiful Birds of the Aftermath', a dark star of the collection, is equally concerned with nature and ritual. A small town impacted by a fatal disaster believe a repeat can be warded off with a bird totem, handmade with care. Stuffed Superb Lyrebirds, made from boxes of eyes and claws by a mildly sceptical girl with only scant memory of the original disaster, are set on a hill to watch over the town.

> "Up, across the valley, ran a ripple of gentle wind, that reached the silvering filamentaries of the birds and ruffled them a little, though not, as Maree remembered, holding her own hair, the way the real birds did, in the videos she had been shown."

In this post-tragedy world, the lines are blurred between what is real and what only has to be believed in. Later, 'A Charm for the World as It Is' offers all kinds of balms; a charm against Trump, for all Cassandras, for the corner shop and all who sail in it.

Among such excellence, some of the stories feel less substantial than those chosen for her debut collection. This is not because of their length, as McClory is a well-established master and celebrant of flash fiction, but because surreal death as the twist in short after short, like a funhouse mirror from different angles, becomes less effective in anticipation and repetitive in collection. I wonder, too, whether characters who are revealed to have supernatural qualities really need them; the eerie inhabitants of 'Distinctive Natural Patterns' are immortal, but their actions need not be to send up the same chill. It is, however, well suited to the humorously titled 'Tommy Wiseau-like Death in 'What Will Be Endured May Yet Be Unbearable', which works the contrast. "...all the lost dogs are dancing on their hind legs. Hai doggies, Death calls down to the street."

Mayhem & Death ends with 'Powdered Milk', a novella about the crew of a submarine test mission (looping back subtly in a character overlap with the first story in the collection.) As things go wrong, cabin fever sets in, and interactions become strained. They team up, turn on one another, count the days in scientific and spy-like voluntary archives and watch food supplies dwindle. It's gripping in the way of sci-fi radio dramas of old.

McClory's words are wide and varied. Her typically atmospheric and occasionally whimsical sentences are as finely crafted as the tension they ramp up, often enlivened with unexpected word choice which may draw from any number of pools; technical, ornithological, or otherwise. At other times, she is succinctly descriptive, such as when a character "breaks through a pool like a finger through an envelope", or practising, more so in this second collection than the first, a cryptic brevity akin to Diane Williams. Beyond being a delight to read, is easy to see why she was recognised as one of Scotland's most accomplished debuts. On these pages is nature—atmospheric and human alike—at its most blustery, given over to its most frightening and fantastical impulses, damp, ripe, and raw.

– Laura Waddell

Roaming in the Gloaming

The Gloaming
Kirsty Logan

Harvill Secker, RRP £12.99, 320pp

Fans of Kirsty Logan will have been eagerly awaiting her fourth novel *The Gloaming*, described on Logan's author website as "a queer mermaid love story set on a remote island that slowly turns its inhabitants to stone". After reading this book in one sitting, I can confirm that readers will be far from disappointed. Logan sweeps the reader into a land where fairy tales and reality collide, where mermaids are real (sort of), and where magic surrounds everything like the sea around the enchanted Scottish island.

We are introduced to the Ross family: Signe, a former prima ballerina, Peter, a boxer with a gentle temperament, and their children: Bee, the youngest and the golden boy of the family; Islay, the eldest, as seductive, rambunctious and fiery as her long red hair; and Mara, the middle child and the protagonist of the story. After tragedy befalls them, each of the family resort to their own coping mechanisms to deal with their grief, whether that be extreme renovation of their castle-like house, rebellion and escape, or, in Mara's case, embarking on an intense and pseudo-magical relationship with Pearl, a mysterious inhabitant of the island who performs as a mermaid in aquatic entertainment shows across the world.

The first thing to note about *The Gloaming* is how the words seem to leap off the page and reach out to you, commanding you to sit down and pay attention. We are not reading a story; rather, we are being told one. Narrated in the style of a fairy tale, Logan expertly weaves the tradition and tedium of living on a remote Scottish island with the intoxicating pull of escape, whether that be a literal escape from the island to the great world beyond, or a metaphorical one in the shape of an irresistible lover. The novel deals with grief, guilt, love and dissatisfaction in a respectful and tender way, mixing magic with mundanity and never once appearing trite or cliché. Logan

truly has mastered the art of the modern fairy tale.

However, the novel does contain some underdeveloped aspects which I desperately wanted to see expanded and resolved. We are given insight into the lives of all of the characters, but not to the extent that we can empathise greatly with them (with the exception of Signe, whose storyline is both touching and heart-breaking). Furthermore, the entire story of Pearl's mermaid life is merely a backstory and is hardly referred to in the novel. It would have done this mermaid love story no harm at all to include more mermaid content, especially as the sections in which Pearl's performing life is depicted are stunningly beautiful.

That being said, since *The Gloaming* is a modern fairy tale, it is important to approach it like one. We don't have to understand why things happen, or how, in order to appreciate just how rich and intricate the story is. We can accept that things may remain unresolved, or fly over our heads, because the only thing we have to do to enjoy a fairy tale is to keep an open mind and accept the story we are being told. Logan sits us down, makes us tea and enchants us with her gorgeous prose, telling us tales of people and places which are both familiar and unfamiliar, compelling us to believe in selkies, magic, and islands that turn its inhabitants to stone. Make sure you set a day aside to read *The Gloaming* – whether it be magic or the *tour-de-force* that is Logan's storytelling, you won't be able to put it down.

– *Rachel Rankin*

Forgotten Gods and Solitude

Iona Lee: Polygon New Poets
Iona Lee

Polygon (2018), RRP £5, 19pp

Frequenters of Scottish spoken word nights and watchers of the Marmite-esque Nationwide poetry adverts will be familiar with Iona Lee: a staggeringly talented and exciting new voice in Scottish poetry. A seasoned performer, Lee has performed at Glastonbury, StAnza and the Edinburgh International Book Festival and won the title of Scottish Slam Champion in 2016. Now, after featuring in Neu! Reekie!'s 2016 poetry anthology *#UntitledTwo*, her eponymous first collection of poems has been published by Polygon as part of their Polygon New Poets series – a series designed to support new poets and introduce their work to a wider audience. On the evidence of this short pamphlet of nine poems, it is fair to say that Lee has proven herself to be an artist who is undoubtedly deserving of this support.

The poems in this collection touch on the deeply personal, from loneliness and religion to mental illness and female solidarity. There is a sense of existential urgency binding the collection together: the final lines of the first poem 'Anicca' implore us to consider that "we all must end / so that others can exist. / That is the cost' and the first lines of 'Solitude' tell us that '[t]ime is terminal and we / must get on with all this living." In spite of this,

the collection itself contains moments of celebration, such as the joy of staying in bed with a lover in 'Wet Hot Happiness' or the excitement of youth and self-discovery in 'It Was Summer Outside', the final poem and undoubtedly the stand out piece of the collection. "We were the new craze" Lee writes. "It was a revelation. / To talk about sex / and women's rights / and broken boys / and wanking."

What is most striking about these poems is how expertly Lee manages to weave the sonority of spoken word with the aesthetic precision of so-called page poetry – a contentious, yet stylistically important, distinction. 'Forgotten Gods' sings with lines which beg to be read aloud, such as "Then I am a run rabbit, run / stunned and staring / at a spyglass sun stream" and "Skin stung hot by the cold – / nipping pin pricks / from the dripping shale cliffs / dipped in hieroglyphic gold". As well as a natural and expert command of the language, the imagery contained within these poems is breath-taking and often funny, rendering them instantly re-readable. Images such as "Dawn breaks like a dropped teacup" are shockingly brilliant, whereas lines such as "white bum like a loaf of bread" and "if you were a metaphor, you'd / probably be the moon, being / all moony in the dark" subvert traditional poetic clichés and inject some much-appreciated comic relief into the otherwise intense collection.

The collection is tight, well-structured and works brilliantly as a unit, and Lee writes in such a confident, fresh and lyrical manner that we are left craving for more. With plans underway for a full

Biographies

Felicity Anderson-Nathan is a writer, tutor and freelancer living in Glasgow. You can find her on twitter @flick_writes.

Nick Athansiou is a Greek-Cypriot Londoner exiled in Glasgow. His work has appeared in *Gutter, Popshot, Valve* and *Quotidian*.

Penny Boxall's collections are *Ship of the Line and Who Goes There?* (2018). She won the 2016 Edwin Morgan Award.

Sheri Benning's most recent collection of poetry is *The Season's Vagrant Light: New and Selected Poems* (Carcanet Press 2015). "Snared" is an excerpt from her novel-in-progress.

Simon K Brown is from the Highlands and won a New Writers Award in 2017. Accost him on Twitter: @SKBwrites

Larry Butler teaches tai-chi, writes poetry & edits www.playspacepublications.com and wordsworkwellscotland.co.uk; and is a trainer in the *Work That Reconnects*.

Rosa Campbell lives in Edinburgh. She is a PhD student, Managing Editor of The Scores & tweets as @rosaetc.

Eleanor Capaldi has been published by *Bare Fiction, Skinned Knee Collective, MIR*, and performed spoken word at festivals including Aye Write.

Vahni Capildeo writes across genres. They live in Edinburgh and are the Douglas Caster Cultural Fellow at the University of Leeds.

Lucy Cathcart Froden is doing a PhD exploring the role of music in integration. She also enjoys parenting/songwriting/podcasting/translating.
www.lumawords.co.uk / @raukarna

AC Clarke's fifth collection, *A Troubling Woman*, came out in 2017, her prizewinning pamphlet, *War Baby*, this year.

Sara Clark is an award-winning writer from Hawick. She is editor of literary magazine, *The Eildon Tree*. @Sara_A_Clark

Colette O'Connor grew up in Kent and is currently compiling a debut poetry collection. Follow her on twitter @MxMacbeth.

Emma Gibb is a poet and short story writer living in Glasgow. Find her @em.lois on Instagram.

David Hale's collection *Dancing under a Bloodless Moon* (Eyewear) is due out soon. Born near Troon, he lives in Gloucestershire.

Melanie Henderson is an Edinburgh-based writer, teacher and former journalist. She has an M Litt (distinction) in creative writing from the University of Stirling.

Bridget Khursheed is a poet and geek based in the Borders and a Scottish Book Trust New Writers Awardee @khursheb

Charles Lang is a poet from Castlemilk in Glasgow. He is a recent English Literature graduate from the University of Edinburgh.

Hannah Lavery is a writer and performer who lives in Dunbar. She was recently awarded a Megaphone Residency by The Workers' Theatre for her Spoken Word Show, *The Drift*.

Iona Lee is a poet, artist and performer from East Lothian. Currently an illustration student at the Glasgow School of Art, her poetry is a distraction from her studies.

William Letford has published two collection of poetry with Carcanet Press, *Bevel*, and *Dirt*. He lives in Stirling.

David Linklater is from Balintore (*Balti/The Bleaching Town*) in the Highlands. He lives and writes in Glasgow.

Marcas Mac an Tuairneir is an award-winning poet, working in Gaelic and English. He has two collections in print and co-authored the pamphlet 'beul-fo-bhonn / heelster-gowdie' (*Tapsalteerie*, 2017) with Stuart A. Paterson.

Agata Maslowska is interested in cultural and linguistic displacement. She received the Hawthornden Fellowship and the Gillian Purvis Award.

Peter McCune has published several short stories and teaches creative writing to people with a history of homelessness and addiction.

Stephen McEwan lives in the Middle East but is planning his escape back to Scotland as you read.

Heather Parry is an Edinburgh-based writer. Her work explores self-deception, transformation and identity. Her first novel is currently under consideration.

Alycia Pirmohamed is a Ph.D. student at the University of Edinburgh, where she is studying poetry by second-generation immigrant writers.

Megan Primrose is a writer, artist, mother and graduate of Glasgow's MLitt Creative Writing Programme. Shortlisted for the Bridport Short Story Prize. She blogs at: www.meganprimrose.co.uk, tweets @bookbeacon.

Olive M Ritch is a prize-winning poet with publications in many literary magazines and anthologies. Her work has also been broadcast on Radio 4.

Mark Russell's most recent publications: *Spearmint & Rescue*, and *Shopping for Punks*; poems in Shearsman, *Blackbox Manifold*, and *The Scores*.

Hamish Scott is from Edinburgh. He has published four Scots poetry collections and won the Scots Prize in the 2015 Wigtown Poetry Competition.

Catherine Simpson's memoir *When I Had a Little Sister* is forthcoming from 4th Estate. Her debut novel *Truestory* was published by Sandstone Press.

Lindsey Shields Waters lives in Glasgow with her family. Her poems have been published in various magazines and anthologies.

Ngũgĩ wa Thiong'o is a Kenyan writer, formerly working in English and now working in Gikuyu. His work includes novels, plays, short stories, and essays. He is the founder and editor of the Gikuyu-language journal *Mũtĩiri*.

Maria Sledmere (@mariaxrose) edits Gilded Dirt and SPAM zine, is a member of A+E Collective and occasional music critic.

Swara Shukla is a Creative Writing graduate from University of Glasgow. Swara works as a Publishing Developer with MageQuill, a publishing platform based in Dornie in the Scottish Highlands.

Dan Spencer's prose appears in journals including *Gutter*, *Flash*, *Brittle Star* and *New Writing Scotland*. He lives in Glasgow. danspencerwriter.wordpress.com

Nicholas Stewart is from East Kilbride. He writes fiction and is working on a new novel.

Jacques Tsianter is currently working on his first novel *Ruin*: psychological thriller and shortlisted entry for the MMU Novella Award.

Sarah Whiteside is a writer and musician whose stories have appeared in *Northwords Now*, *New Writing Scotland*, and elsewhere.

Jay Whittaker's first collection, *Wristwatch*, was published by Cinnamon in 2017. She recently read at StAnza and Interrobang. jaywhittaker.uk@jaywhittapoet

Kevin Williamson is a writer of poetry & prose, creative director of Neu! Reekie!, once of the Rebel Inc parish.

Ross Wilson's first full collection of poetry, *Line Drawing*, will be published by Smokestack Books in December 2018.

Hannah Van Hove is a writer and researcher from Brussels who lives and works in Glasgow.